CLOSE TO HOME

Dedication

To Harry McCree, whose
authority and effort allowed the service
to be developed

CLOSE TO HOME:

a local housing service and its impact
on the lives of nine adults
with severe and profound mental handicaps

David Felce

Sandy Toogood

First published 1988

(BIMH Publications is the publishing office of the
British Institute of Mental Handicap, Registered Charity No. 264786)

Published and distributed by: **BIMH Publications,**
Foley Industrial Park,
Stourport Road,
Kidderminster,
Worcs. DY11 7QG

ISBN 0 906054 65 6

Typeset and printed by: Birmingham Printers (1982) Ltd.,
Stratford Street North, Birmingham B11 1BY

Contents

Acknowledgements

To the people described in this book, whom we have come to respect.

To the staff involved in the house since its opening, whose contribution we have represented here.

To the families, who have allowed us to make personal observations out of their commitment to improve the circumstances experienced by people with mental handicaps.

To Judith Jenkins and Jim Mansell, who worked with us in the provision and running of the house.

To the managers of the service who supported the development, in particular Don Dell, Peter Wilcock, Mike Wratten, and John Clugston.

To Sara Graham, who suggested we write this type of account and who played a central role in the management of the DHSS funded research involvement in the service.

To Alan Tyne, Judith Jenkins, and Harry McCree for reading earlier drafts and giving us helpful and encouraging comments.

To Sandra Collingwood, for typing and retyping the manuscript.

We hope we have recorded facts accurately. The perspective and opinions are ours, as are any errors.

David Felce
Sandy Toogood

CHAPTER 1

Introduction — about this book

This book is about one ordinary house in a residential street near the centre of a small market town, called for the purposes of anonymity 10 Summerton Road, Merton. It has been home for nine adults with severe or profound mental handicaps who have local ties. It has also provided the setting for a research project designed to investigate ways of running this kind of residence as an alternative to large mental handicap hospitals. Although the suggestion of community-based alternatives to institutional care is not new, few such schemes exist for adults with the most severe handicaps who are in need of residential care. There is still some controversy about the desirability or feasibility of schemes of this kind, hence the relevance of continuing research and development.

The research programme included setting up the house and working closely with staff in how to run it. A research evaluation was also carried out, using various objective indices, of the day-to-day life and activity of the adults for whom the house became a home. References to the various evaluation reports are given at the end of the chapter.

This book, however, contains a different kind of account. It is a factual description of the story of the house, told through the experiences of the nine adults who lived in it. It is our perception of the human stories behind the research. Although the book concentrates on the experiences of individual people, its overall theme is the house and the orientation of the service; for, despite the detail, it is inevitably an account written from our viewpoint as service providers. The adults whose lives are described largely lack language and so cannot give an account of their own views or feelings, explain their own behaviour, or say what they would like to happen in the future. We have tried to maintain an impression of observing their lives from the outside rather than appearing to put forward opinions or interpretations as if they were their own.

It is important to keep in mind that the descriptions cover only a short period in the lives of the adults concerned. Parts of each person's story have been selected and discussed; parts which seem to have special relevance in relation to issues commonly raised in the current debate about residential services for adults with severe or profound mental handicaps and disruptive behaviour. Throughout this century adults with disabilities of this kind, particularly those whose behaviour is considered aggressive, asocial, or strange, have been accommodated in segregated institutions away from the villages, towns, and cities in which most of us live. Slowly the climate has been changing and there is now greater support for the notion that everyone, unless found guilty of a criminal offence, should have the opportunity of living within the community in an ordinary residential area, and of experiencing the normal patterns and responsibilities of daily life. But, as with any process of social change, there is always a debate. Questions have been raised in connection with the practicality of implementing the community care policy: "How can adults with such severe handicaps live a normal life in the community?"; "How can difficult behaviour be managed?". There have also been questions about whether there are any advantages to the adults concerned: "How much will someone with a profound handicap respond to a normal pattern of life?"; "Isn't the tranquility of a sheltered institutional life more suitable for adults who cannot cope independently with the stresses of modern society?".

Before beginning our account we must declare our own view of the development of human behaviour. We think it can best be understood by looking at the day-to-day interaction between the personal characteristics of individuals, their current situation, and what they have learned from past experience. So we would not look for answers to the above questions just by studying and classifying the personal characteristics of people considered to be mentally handicapped, or by cataloguing differences between various types of environment and making assumptions about how they may affect behaviour. We think that the answers to these questions can best, and perhaps may only, be found by gaining experience of different types of service alternatives and finding out how each one benefits or fails to benefit the people it serves. Take the question: "How can difficult behaviour be managed?". We think the best chance of finding out the answer is to design and implement a service which attempts to do so, and to learn from the successes and failures experienced along the way. Little will be learned by excluding from the start people with difficult behaviour, on a prediction that they may not be managed. From our standpoint there has been too much rhetoric and too little development to date; too few practical attempts to test alternative ways of providing residential services.

It seems to us that the debate on this major change in social policy is still being conducted on the whole in vague, imprecise statements, with little empirical evidence being brought to bear on the validity of the propositions discussed. We wrote this book, therefore, because we thought a useful contribution to the debate would be as careful a description as we could manage of the personal circumstances and experiences of some adults with severe and profound handicaps and how those changed when the service provided for them was changed.

Research has tended, in the name of objectivity, to avoid detailed personal accounts. As people involved in research, we do not wish to belittle the importance of objective evaluation. We believe scientific method is crucial to the development of social policy. The credibility of the accounts given in this book would be diminished if we were not able also to list a series of research reports at the end of this Introduction which attempt to follow the rules of scientific methodology. However, we also believe that much of the *quality* of the change in the lives of the adults who have lived at 10 Summerton Road would go unrecorded if we had restricted ourselves just to reporting the information gathered by the objective research measures employed. Although our research data are important to us, it was the *quality of the adults' experience* which these data reflected that gladdened our hearts and encouraged us to believe the service was developing in the right way. When we interpret our own research data we have concrete pictures of real people doing real things as they go about the business of their daily life. Our reason for writing this book is to attempt to help others view the service development, and the research of it, through the eyes of those who have been closely connected with it.

Words of caution

This book is a record of the accomplishment of a single service setting in terms of the change it brought about for a few adults with handicaps. It shows what is possible; it illustrates an orientation; it highlights where improvements are needed and where problems still exist. However, there are dangers in over-generalising or simplifying. There need to be many more examples of high quality services and further work on what distinguishes a high quality service from a mediocre or poor one before we can be satisfied that such services can be delivered routinely to those who need them.

The house described is an example of a new type of service. If new services are to be different from those that have gone before them, they must be operated in different ways. This necessitates competence in new areas, and it is likely that the skills required in providing community-based services for people with the most severe handicaps will be relatively thin on the ground for some time to come. The growth in high quality residential services, therefore, may need to be gradual. Also, the specification of such a service is complex. It involves aspects of size, building design, location, staffing, operational policy, job descriptions, management relationships and support arrangements, staff training, and working methods. The residential service to be described is not just an ordinary house in the community, although that is part of it. Simply establishing a small community residence using ordinary housing, but without the careful arrangements made in other respects, would not necessarily have similar benefits.

Although the accounts given in this book are lengthy and we have tried to be both detailed and precise, the information contained is selective. Our interpretation of some of the information, and our analysis of why people's behaviour changed, is opinion. It may be considered thoughtful and convincing by some readers and not by others. Although one author is a research scientist and scientific evaluation of the house and the adults is available, this does not mean that the accounts given in this book are scientific. For example, the fact that we have precise measurements of the rate of change of some disruptive behaviours does not mean that we know for sure why the behaviour changed. Proof requires appropriate (and ethical) use of experimental design, in addition to measurement and careful interpretation. Unfortunately some useful research on individual change was beyond our resources given the other types of evaluation we were conducting; thus, the majority of our explanations of change remain speculative.

We have tried to be thoughtful and honest in our accounts and to fit our knowledge of what was done by service staff to our knowledge of how it affected the service users. In doing so we have brought to bear our knowledge of the scientific literature on how people's behaviour may be affected by their environmental experience. We have not attempted to cite the literature, but rather to concentrate on telling an uninterrupted story. Our understanding of human behaviour is derived from the literature of applied behaviour analysis. However, we do not profess to have a complete knowledge of this, or an indisputable interpretation of it. Moreover, it is certain that some of our interpretation is wisdom developed after the event. Neither we nor our service colleagues were always quite as smart or certain as the impression given in the pages which follow.

It is, however, true to say that we had a commitment to making community care work. We hope that the difficulties and problems, as well as the successes, are adequately reflected in our descriptions, so as to make the accounts given true-to-life and to convince readers of our honest endeavour to describe accurately what really happened.

About the house

We sought to establish at 10 Summerton Road a residential service which set out to achieve a clearly defined purpose. As it was an intensively staffed service for people with severe and profound mental handicaps this meant concentrating on how staff did their job. We tried to influence this by establishing procedures for staff to follow and by providing specific staff training. The house, as a service, can be represented by three strands: its orientation, its structure, and the staff procedures followed.

The stated orientation of the service was defined once the prime function of the house in the lives of its users had been determined. We considered how ordinary people typically conduct their lives, and how having a mental handicap might alter their experience. We decided that the prime function of the house as a residential service for adults with severe and profound handicaps was to provide people with a permanent home; therefore, the primary aim was to open opportunities and give support to the people living in the house so that they might experience a "normal" pattern of home life. This pattern was to include contribution and responsibility as well as comfort, leisure, security, and close social relationships. Specifically, we thought that one of the major experiences of people with such severe handicaps was a difficulty in being fully occupied and stimulated throughout the day in activities which usually preoccupy those of us considered to be non-handicapped. Our central objective, therefore, was the provision of opportunity, choice, and support, which would result in the adults being meaningfully occupied for the bulk of their time. It is only when such an objective is achieved that leisure and rest can take on their true meanings.

Another specific objective was for the adults to continue to develop skills and independence as a result of their experience of the service. Moreover, it was intended that the service would be competent to alter patterns of socially inappropriate, damaging behaviour, and replace them with more constructive alternatives for the benefit of the individuals concerned. Lastly, home life was seen within a social, community context. Community integration was a specific aim, embracing the use of the amenities of the local town, the maintenance of family ties, and the development of friendships and personal pursuits outside of the home.

The task, then, was to provide a service structure which facilitated these objectives. We wanted the physical design, location, staffing, and organisational arrangements of the house to reflect client considerations rather than traditional or bureaucratic structures of the service-providing agency. We wanted to ensure that, unless specialist service arrangements were known to enhance the quality of client experience, the adults living in the house would share the arrangements chosen by the broad mass of the population. We wanted an efficient organisation, and one in which the staff on whom the adults depended had few obstacles placed in their way, so enabling them to make all sorts of beneficial arrangements for the individuals they served. We wanted a local service so that families and friends were nearby; and we wanted the house to be as close as possible to the centre of town to enable maximum use of its amenities. We found that it was possible to achieve many of these objectives within the constraints of the service providing agency, the National Health Service.

The house is a four-bedroomed, detached property sited among other similar houses in a residential street close to the centre of Merton. Conscious efforts were made to maintain the appearance of the house as a private dwelling but two additional bedrooms and an extra bathroom were added to the ground floor at the rear of the property for the benefit of adults who could not manage stairs. There is a mature garden with lawn, flower borders, and established shrubs. Decoration and furnishings are to a standard that would be expected in a well-to-do home, and equipment and household effects are geared to giving the impression that the house is simply the home of several ordinary, mature adults. No extra safeguards against accidental damage or injury are built into the physical environment, and the adults have access to domestic appliances, electrical equipment, and breakable ornaments. The onus of ensuring the adults' safety and exposing them to only a reasonable level of risk is placed on staff. The expectation is that people can care for themselves and their surroundings if they are given sufficient support to enable them to undertake that responsibility.

There are still some obtrusive features, mainly to do with safety against fire, but many common problems in the appearance of service buildings have been avoided. Instead of vinyl, the living room furniture is upholstered in cloth; the kitchen is fitted with ordinary wood and laminate units; and the cooker, refrigerator, and other household appliances are domestic rather than commercial models. The living room, hall, stairs, and bedrooms have wall-to-wall wool-mixture carpets. Ornaments, plants, and other personal decorative touches abound. Despite the rather large number of people living in the house, its appearance has been well-kept over several years.

The house provides eight residential places and, therefore, its inhabitants still live in a large group by normal standards. At first two places were reserved for short stay provision for people living nearby with their parents. This was contrary to our original intention but had been requested by the representatives of a local voluntary society. Later, this was reduced to one place. There are 11 whole-time-equivalent staff posts, nine day staff and four half-time night staff. Within the allocation of day staff are included the person-in-charge and the deputy. There are no separate cooks or domestics as it is intended that the adults have every possible opportunity to participate in the daily round of household chores which their lives generate. The staff have considerable freedom to manage their day-to-day activity. They have control over budget expenditure, which is vital if they are to be free to shop with the adults and arrange for the upkeep of the house and garden. However, given their autonomy, careful effort has been given to staff training and the structuring of working methods.

For every theme in the statement of orientation, we wanted to design a staff procedure explicitly directed towards attaining that objective. The theme of individual development is reflected in systems of individual programming. *Individual programme planning* (IPP) meetings (Jenkins *et al.*, 1988) give a comprehensive review of the priority needs for each adult to which the service should address itself. These encompass needs for wider experiences, improved health, improved or more mature appearance, learning, friendships, wider pursuits, and greater community involvement. The meetings comprise a multi-disciplinary group of professionals, each of whom has an active role in the care of the adult being discussed, together with the adult and the adult's relatives or advocate. Health and social services personnel set objectives for each adult together.

Where educational goals are concerned, programming within the house is conducted at two levels of intensity. In a "broad-brush" approach, which we term *opportunity planning* (Toogood *et al.*, 1983), several (6-10) behavioural objectives are set for each adult every fortnight and written on a single chart which contains a recording grid spanning the next 14 days. Staff build in opportunities to practise each behavioural objective during the adult's day and record implementation and success on the grid. Opportunity plans do not specify the method of teaching but they do ensure that, irrespective of which staff are on duty, emerging skills that need to be worked on every day are targeted and recorded. At a more detailed level, staff also set and follow individual teaching programmes, using the *Bereweeke Skill-Teaching System*. Skills to be taught are analysed into a series of discrete weekly steps, each one of which is then programmed on an activity chart. The activity chart sets out the teaching objective for the week, the method of teaching and the number of teaching sessions per day. A record shows implementation and the adult's progress towards the goal. This more intensive level of teaching is used for goals where staff have already experienced (or predict) lack of success with opportunity planning. The *Bereweeke System* materials have recently been revised in a second edition (Mansell *et al.*, 1986) which includes a staff handbook, and assessment checklists for children and adults. The checklist for adults (Felce, *et al.*, 1986) has been specifically designed to translate early developmental skills into activities which are appropriate for adults rather than children.

Skill acquisition as an objective for people with mental handicaps is rarely questioned, presumably because it reverses the defining condition. Skill usage, or engagement in activity, is the important consequence of capability, however, and this can be viewed as a fundamental indicator of the quality of a person's life and of the care given. The service environment (including the pattern of staff activity) can be said to be appropriate for someone to the extent to which it supports the translation of that person's skills, however limited, into meaningful activity. Choice can only be said to be present if the environment provides the support to create real opportunities for individuals to participate productively. Important though individual planning and teaching are, the proportion of a person's day which is spent following a written programme or an activity derived from a plan is low. This is not necessarily a criticism — it may actually be appropriate for adults, for whom some balance between continuing to learn how to live life and actually living it should be drawn. Therefore, if following individual programmes is going to be a small part of a person's day, what remains of the utmost importance to overall service quality are the routine interactions and orientation of staff. How much do staff support individuals' involvement? Which behaviours of the people in their care do they motivate? How much opportunity do staff deny people with mental handicaps by doing tasks themselves? However sophisticated individual programming may be, it may be of little account if these general aspects of staff performance are poorly determined.

Procedures have therefore been established in the house to help staff take a systematic approach to the routine organisation of the adults' day and the allocation of household tasks and caring duties throughout their time on duty. Promotion of staff performance has involved three strategies: establishing a basic organisational structure; training staff in the philosophy of the service and means of promoting the adults' independence and participation in events and activities; and establishing a form of monitoring by which staff can review how successful they have been in supporting the adults in a range of community and household activities. Parts of the staff induction training cover organisational structures at a very simple level — how to organise shopping, cleaning and cooking, staff rotas, communication systems, and household standards. Staff training also covers the behavioural principles of staff:adult interaction, including the use of antecedent conditions to help to encourage adults' engagement in activity and learning situations throughout the day. Instruction, demonstration, physical prompting and complete physical guidance, paired with the task analytic skill of breaking a complex behaviour into small, discrete stages, is used to help people with even the most severe handicaps to participate effectively.

Staff interaction with the adults is an important motivating factor. Attention, particularly praise, should be directed towards adults' meaningful occupation as opposed to passivity, or unpurposeful or inappropriate behaviour. Even though this may not always be sufficient to motivate adaptive behaviour in the adults, staff awareness of how they distribute their attention remains a desirable general accomplishment. Day-to-day organisation and planning of adults' activity is achieved by a flexible system of timetabling and allocating staff responsibility, which also involves staff in recording and summarising the activities in which each adult participates within the household. Like other monitoring mechanisms incorporated within the methods of care (such as the implementation and success rates of teaching in the *Bereweeke* system and the recording of community events), this provides feedback data for review of care practices in the weekly staff meetings.

About the chapters

Nine adults have lived in the house from its opening to the time of writing, a period of over three years. Five were involved with the service at its start and a chapter is devoted to each of their stories. These chapters share a similarity in format because, although concerned with different people, they illustrate the response of a single service to the diverse needs of each individual. Overlap between the chapters reflects the common experiences of people with severe handicaps: the tendency towards childish appearance, low expectation, absence of responsibility, lack of opportunity for participation or development, and the likelihood of strange or anti-social behaviour being interpreted as deranged or deliberately oppositional rather than sensible from the individual's viewpoint. Each chapter concentrates on the service response to an individual; a response which seeks to enhance social status by helping each one achieve an appearance, responsibility, and degree of participation in daily life that is appropriate to that person's chronological age, irrespective of mental age. This response also assumes that, within their current capabilities, people with mental handicaps are wise, and their behaviour serves a positive function. If the service is to be wise, that is, if it is to help its clients to develop new ways of behaving which are more advantageous to them as individuals, it will need to seek to understand their wisdom.

Service responses are largely determined by the personal characteristics of clients. Each chapter, therefore, contains some description of the adults whose stories are being told. Some readers may feel that these descriptions are clinical appraisals; pictures of how people present as "problems" to the helping service, devoid of human warmth. Simple explanations are often the best, and the simplest here would be that we lack the novelist's skill to conjure an accurate picture of each person. But other thoughts are relevant. It is important to convey to readers what the adults did or did not do, and how they each chose to spend their time, for this is how service staff experienced them. A metaphorical description based on personality traits does not do this. It also fails to capture the impact of having a mental handicap. People with severe mental handicaps have personalities: they may be cooperative, enthusiastic, highly sociable, charming, withdrawn, self-reliant, awkward, or whatever. What is not conveyed by these terms is the means by which those people express their personalities. Personality traits can be expressed through behavioural abilities which are completely beyond the people described in this book. It is relevant, both to the understanding of the significance of the service response and to the place that these accounts have in the debate on service design, that readers gain a correct impression of the lack of ability of the people described. Their lack of communicative language for other than basic needs constrains our descriptions as we have no direct access into their views on life, likes, dislikes, or preferences. We have tried to refrain from expressing our own thoughts as if they were the views of the adults or an indication of their personal characteristics.

As there is so much common ground in the experience of many people with mental handicaps there is a danger of repetition from one chapter to the next. We have therefore been more selective in describing the stories of the four people who have spent less time in the house. We have concentrated on a particular aspect of each one's experience which we think may have some general relevance.

The material in all the chapters, both in terms of the adults' experiences and the service responses, can be related to issues of service philosophy. Occasionally we interrupt the narrative to explore such issues further. We hope that readers who wish to continue the narrative at these points will excuse our digressions.

REFERENCES, RESEARCH PAPERS, AND OTHER DESCRIPTIVE ACCOUNTS OF THE SMALL HOUSE SERVICE

de Kock, U., Felce, D., Saxby, H., Thomas, M. Community and family contact: an evaluation of small community homes for adults with severe and profound mental handicaps. *Mental Handicap Research*, 1988; **1**, 127-140.

Felce, D. Accommodating adults with severe and profound mental handicaps: comparative revenue costs. *Mental Handicap*, 1986; **14**, 104-107.

Felce, D., de Kock, U. Accommodating adults with severe and profound mental handicaps: comparative capital costs. *Mental Handicap*, 1986; **14**, 26-29.

Felce, D., de Kock, U., Repp, A. An eco-behavioural comparison of small community-based houses and traditional large hospitals for severely and profoundly mentally handicapped adults. *Applied Research in Mental Retardation*, 1986; **7**, 393-408.

Felce, D., de Kock, U., Thomas, M., Saxby, H. Change in adaptive behaviour of severely and profoundly mentally handicapped adults in different residential settings. *British Journal of Psychology*, 1986; **77**, 489-501.

Felce, D., Jenkins, J., de Kock, U., Mansell, J. *The Bereweeke Skill-Teaching System: a goal-setting checklist for adults*. Windsor: NFER/Nelson, 1986.

Felce, D., Mansell, J., de Kock, U., Toogood, S., Jenkins, J. Housing severely and profoundly mentally handicapped adults. *Hospital and Health Services Review*, 1984; **80**, 170-174.

Felce, D., Mansell, J., Jenkins, J., de Kock, U. *The Bereweeke Skill-Teaching System (2nd edn.)*. Windsor: NFER/Nelson, 1986.

Felce, D., Saxby, H., de Kock, U., Repp, A., Ager, A., Blunden, R. To what behaviours do attending adults respond?: a replication. *American Journal of Mental Deficiency*, 1987; **91**, 496-504.

Felce, D., Thomas, M., de Kock, U., Repp, A., Ager, A., Blunden, R. Staff:client ratios and their effects on staff interactions and client behaviours in 12 facilities for severely and profoundly mentally handicapped adults. *Research in Developmental Disabilities*, 1988 (in press).

Felce, D., Thomas, M., de Kock, U., Saxby, H., Repp, A. An ecological comparison of small community-based houses and traditional institutions for severely and profoundly mentally handicapped adults: II Physical settings and the use of opportunities. *Behaviour Research and Therapy*, 1985; **23**, 337-348.

Jenkins, J., Felce, D., Toogood, S., Mansell, J., de Kock, U. *Individual Programme Planning*. Kidderminster: BIMH Publications, 1988.

Mansell, J., Felce, D., Jenkins, J., de Kock, U., Toogood, S. A Wessex home-from-home. *Nursing Times*, 1983; 3 Aug., 51-56.

Mansell, J., Felce, D., Jenkins, J., Flight, C., Dell, D. *The Bereweeke Skill-Teaching System: handbook*. Windsor: NFER/Nelson, 1986.

Mansell, J., Jenkins, J., Felce, D., de Kock, U. Measuring the activity of severely and profoundly mentally handicapped adults in ordinary housing. *Behaviour Research and Therapy*, 1984; **22**, 23-29.

Mansell, J., Jenkins, J., Felce, D., de Kock, U., Toogood, S. *A Staffed House for Eight Mentally Handicapped Adults*. Chelmsford: Graves Medical Audio/Visual Library, 1984.

Saxby, H., Felce, D., Harman, M., Repp, A. The maintenance of client activity and staff:client interaction in small community homes for severely and profoundly mentally handicapped adults: a two-year follow-up. *Behavioral Psychotherapy*, 1988 (in press).

Saxby, H., Thomas, M., Felce, D., de Kock, U. The use of shops, cafés and public houses by severely and profoundly mentally handicapped adults. *British Journal of Mental Subnormality*, 1986; **32**, 69-81.

Thomas, M., Felce, D., de Kock, U., Saxby, H., Repp, A. The activity of staff and of severely and profoundly mentally handicapped adults in residential settings of different sizes. *British Journal of Mental Subnormality*, 1986; **32**, 82-92.

Toogood, S., Jenkins, J., Felce, D., de Kock, U. *Opportunity Plans*. 1983 (Unpubl.). Avail. from: D. Felce, BIMH, Wolverhampton Road, Kidderminster, Worcs. DY10 3PP.

CHAPTER 2

Shirley White — a new home and out to work

Shirley White moved from a large mental handicap hospital to 10 Summerton Road, Merton on Sunday November 1, 1981. It was the beginning of a considerably improved life, which brought her back near her father and two sisters who had kept in touch with her throughout the thirty-five years she had spent away. Shirley had lived in hospital since the age of six. For almost thirty years she had lived in the "locked" ward for female "patients". When she moved she was nearly forty-one years old. When first arriving as a child, her new home was still officially called a "colony". A year later, following the formation of the National Health Service, the colony became a hospital which, during the next three decades, saw the development of the mental handicap nursing profession, a greater proliferation of psychiatrists, and the growth of psychological and paramedical involvement.

Shirley's home, which she shared with more than thirty other women, was a two-storey hospital villa, a detached ward set among others in a country estate. On the ground floor was one large living area and dining room. Upstairs was a large dormitory in which Shirley had a bed and a small bedside locker. In this she kept her clothes and a few personal possessions such as her dolls. There was only one dormitory, and to this day it is not partitioned to give any privacy. There were some small side-rooms which were used to isolate people who were "very difficult". Many of the people who lived in the locked ward had disturbed behaviour, including Shirley herself. It was the female "back" ward, into which women who had been hard to manage elsewhere in the hospital had been collected. People living in it were detached; many showed bizarre patterns of behaviour. It is difficult to imagine how staff could avoid being overwhelmed by their task of trying to create a normal social environment and a normal daily round of purposeful occupation. Here was a situation in which people who had particular difficulties in relating one to another had been deliberately grouped together.

Shirley is profoundly deaf. She is also blind in one eye and poorly sighted in the other. Her notes record an estimated intelligence quotient of approximately 20, but this is hard to accept given Shirley as we now know her. She was fully ambulant, had good motor control of all limbs, could take herself to the toilet, feed herself, and could wash and dress herself independently to the standards required in hospital. However she had no means of communication at all, being mute unless in a state of extreme agitation and having been taught no form of signing or symbolic language.

In an unsympathetic social setting, with no means of communication, unable to hear, and with limited sight, she naturally had difficulties in filling her day constructively. Although competent in her own basic self-care, she had no hobby skills, no work, and no ability to converse with which to occupy the intervals between getting up, mealtimes, and going to bed. The environment in which she lived emphasised rather than alleviated her personal handicaps. Social isolation, peculiar behaviour, and lack of meaningful activity were usual. In order to establish simple basic opportunities for people living on the ward special arrangements had to be made. Even then, they could affect the lives of only a few. Just before she moved, a change in ward organisation had allowed Shirley and three other women to eat their meals separately from the others and help to wash up afterwards.

Although the villa was called a "locked" ward, this did not mean that the women were denied access to the hospital grounds. Indeed it is hard to be precise about the exact meaning of the designation "locked", or what purpose the emphasis on security served. The clearest practical effect was to create the "back" ward identity and the grouping together of people considered to be mentally ill as well as mentally handicapped. At the time of her leaving, Shirley's main and favourite activity was wheeling a small doll's pram around the hospital grounds. She was not considered likely to stray off the hospital campus. In fact, it was said that she clung to the hospital as her source of security. It was confidently predicted that Shirley would become distressed and extremely agitated if taken outside the hospital. For this reason, she had not been included in recreational outings or taken on trips to the local community. Nor, on the advice of staff, did her relatives do anything other than visit her within the hospital.

With no organised daytime activity Shirley spent much of her time walking in the hospital grounds. When in the ward, she passed her day in self-stimulatory, rhythmic body- and head-rocking, and walking in small circles. Her notes make it clear that this was her characteristic activity. The emptiness of her hospital life was dramatically illustrated to us shortly after she had moved. Shirley made a curious sign with her fingers. It involved holding one palm flat in front of her and tracing round and round it in circles with a finger of her other hand. As Shirley appeared to use no form of communication, it was thought important to investigate every gesture as having possible meaning. Staff at 10 Summerton Road telephoned the ward staff to ask their opinion. They too had noticed this curious behaviour but said that they did not know what it meant, other than possibly signalling an intent to walk round in circles. This reply gave a powerful image of the long-term nature of the setting in which Shirley had lived. It produced a strong impression of the poverty of the institutional environment where such a behaviour could be a dominant preference. Worse still, it showed the kind of activity that is considered reasonable in such settings and is tolerated for months and years.

Part of the reason why Shirley lived where she did was that she was very disruptive. She injured herself and was aggressive to others. Periodically, she hit her head and attacked her face near her eyes. During the day she sometimes hit other women who approached her. At night, she had outbursts of attacking others and tipping them out of bed. Although records of this disturbed behaviour are frequent in her notes, there was no specific programme of management. All that was noted was an assessment of the severity of the problem, which varied from entry to entry. At the time of initial discussion as to whom 10 Summerton Road might serve, a psychological report on Shirley's behaviour suggested that the problems had lessened. It attributed the improvement to the fact that Shirley had been given a new doll's pram to push round the hospital grounds. However, a few months later the severity of her disturbed behaviour returned, consistent not only with a possible decline in pleasure derived from her new pram but also with the long-term picture of fluctuation given in the notes. Shirley was prescribed a regular tranquilliser, with back-up dosages of a second tranquilliser and a sedative to be used as required.

Apart from such medication and the care of the ward staff, there was little evidence of attempts to help Shirley live a more full or satisfying life. There is no record of any assessment of either hearing or sight during her thirty-year stay in hospital, despite considerable sensory handicaps. Her deafness is, in fact, irremediable. Her poor eye-sight, however, had received surgical treatment in early childhood. Her father remembers her having a number of operations when she was an infant and the opthalmologist who assessed her after the move to 10 Summerton Road confirmed the presence of operative scar tissue in her eyes. As a young child she had glasses which her father says she took with her on admission to hospital. Sometime during her years there they were lost; and Shirley came to 10 Summerton Road without this simple aid to alleviate her conspicuous impairment. Even with glasses, which she was prescribed in the second month after moving to her new home, her eyesight is poor. Nevertheless, they have made a considerable difference to the precision with which she can conduct her life. For example, if Shirley wished to pick up a moderately-sized object such as a salt-cellar, without her glasses, she would pat the surface of the table with fingers outstretched until they made contact with it. Wearing glasses, she can pick up the object deftly in one go.

Throughout her time in hospital, Shirley's father and two sisters visited her regularly. It was a seventy- to eighty-mile round trip, so they could only manage to visit monthly. Shirley shows a strong affection for her family, and her family for her, as is obvious to anyone seeing them together. While she was in hospital, her family visited her in the ward. Believing that Shirley did not wish to leave the hospital they confined any trips out together to the hospital grounds. This widely-held opinion cast doubt upon whether Shirley would like to move to 10 Summerton Road. It also gave cause for concern about whether the forty-mile journey could be achieved safely and pleasantly.

Making the transfer: moving to a new house

There are at least two perspectives on the benefits of an alternative service such as the one proposed in this book for a person in Shirley's situation. There is the view of the staff who have worked to establish the home, who have held to their task in the face of the claims and counter claims of supporters and detractors of the new venture. They possess a genuine expectation that the quality of life of people receiving the new service will be enhanced by moving. Their commitment implies a belief that such a service would be good for anyone in Shirley's situation. But there is also the individual's perspective. For Shirley the move involved changing one home, of thirty years' standing, for another. What is there to suggest the general arguments are correct in every individual case?

As far as Shirley is concerned the evidence appeared to point to a preference for staying in hospital. She was said to view the confines of the hospital campus as a major part of her own personal security; an opinion which, stated in general terms, conforms closely to the notion that hospitals provide a genuine asylum for people who are dependent, who would be unsettled by the demands of the outside world. Shirley's favourite activity was wheeling a doll's pram around the extensive hospital grounds. So favoured was this activity that the purchase of a new pram was linked by a psychologist to a general mood change that brought about a temporary reduction in disruptive behaviour. When considering people for the move to 10 Summerton Road it was not at all clear how this issue would be handled; but it was fairly obvious that Shirley would not be able to push her pram in the same manner around the streets of Merton. Moreover, the garden of an ordinary house would hardly provide the same scope or exercise. Yet, balancing these considerations was a strong sense of the futility of Shirley's current way of life.

It was knowledge of the lives led by people like Shirley which had convinced us that a more meaningful existence should be created for them. Moreover, it was our belief, and this has been confirmed by our experience of working with Shirley and the other adults who have lived in the house, that it is too constraining to judge individuals' possible preferences for the future by their choice of activity in their current situation, or as it reflects their past development.

Of course Shirley's relatives were consulted. They were not members of any local voluntary society and were not actively involved either in support for service change or in defence of existing large hospitals. They were able to hear the proposal that Shirley move to a home near them without hostility and without immediately considering the notion impossible or absurd. (This was not always the case with families. We soon discovered that it was necessary to decide whose rights the service must support; for what appears to us to be in a person's best interests may not always correspond with the views of family members.) Shirley's relatives felt that her happiness should be the determining factor in the decision. They were worried that, as she had lived in hospital for so long, she might find any change unsettling. They, however, viewed themselves as ill-informed to make a judgement on the alternatives available for Shirley and, probably over-generously, credited us as being the "experts" and left the decision to us.

We were confident that in the long-term Shirley would benefit from moving to a better home; but we had qualms about the first few weeks. These qualms were natural but probably unnecessary. Throughout our involvement in first setting up larger community-based units, and then small homes like 10 Summerton Road, noticeably negative reactions to leaving a large hospital by people with severe and profound mental handicaps have been rare. On the other hand, there have been several expressions of positive preference for the new situation. Given the views of Shirley's relatives and the staff at the hospital, an offer of a trial period in 10 Summerton Road was made, with the opportunity of a transfer back to the large hospital should she seem particularly unhappy after moving. This offer was made with every intent that members of the service team would act as advocates for the welfare of Shirley herself; but there were bureaucratic constraints which meant that a return might not have been possible. The hospital in which Shirley lived was in a health district which was keen to limit its service to citizens from within its own boundaries. Once an alternative residential place was offered for a resident from another health district, readmission was not guaranteed. Three years later, the health district concerned decided to close the hospital in which Shirley had lived. Knowing at the time the direction in which its policy was going, we were aware that some change in her residential circumstances was likely to occur at some point anyway. Shirley was without doubt a victim of the "geographic chaos" of the large hospital system. If she had to move, it seemed to us that 10 Summerton Road was the best option.

The decision, of course, could not be ours alone. We felt we must consult Shirley herself as the client; the person who is the reason for the service. It should never be assumed that people with mental handicaps are incapable of representing a rational view, however handicapped they may be or however low their tested mental age. It would be too glib to suggest that consultation with clients is an alternative to every other form of consideration. People with severe mental handicaps have real problems in understanding what is said to them and in articulating a view; it is sometimes extremely difficult to know how much they have understood and what significance to give to any answer. There were considerable difficulties in consulting Shirley. She was profoundly deaf, she was mute, she had no recognisable means of communication. As it was believed that she would find leaving the hospital grounds traumatic, the suggestion that she visit 10 Summerton Road a number of times to gauge her reaction before actually moving was not considered feasible. In order to try to explain the situation to her, we made a photograph album of pictures of the new house, some of which had Shirley's relatives in them. We visited Shirley and attempted to tell her as best we could, by gesture and by showing her the photographs, that she could move from the hospital. We gave her the photograph album to keep. We could not tell whether her smiling response was out of enjoyment of the social contact, pleasure from the photographs of her relatives, or whether it represented any form of view about the proposed move. After the visit, ward staff reported that Shirley was proud of the album and liked to show them the pictures. Again it was difficult to interpret whether this indicated pleasure in the possession or at the prospect of moving.

In the event, Shirley moved on Sunday, 1 November 1981. She was collected by a member of the new care staff in a car driven by a parent of one of the other adults who would be moving to the house. A member of the hospital ward staff accompanied her. The predicted stress on leaving the hospital did not occur; the journey was straightforward and uneventful; and Shirley arrived at her new home to find her father and two sisters waiting to greet her.

Early days in 10 Summerton Road

Shirley's family remember her arrival that afternoon:

"We were scared, afraid that Shirley would not settle in. We felt that we shared the responsibility for the decision to offer Shirley the opportunity to move and were worried it would not turn out well. She had been there a long time.

She arrived with a member of staff and a nurse from the hospital. She appeared bewildered and agitated. Although she was wearing new clothes for the occasion, they were ill-fitting but greatly improved on her previous standard of dress. Her shoes didn't fit. She seemed to derive some comfort from seeing us.

She didn't behave the way we thought she would. It must have been strange, it was the first real move in her life. It was different — before she never wanted to go out — she never seemed to — she seemed frightened and gave an impression of insecurity. We were surprised by Shirley on her first day. Her attitude all that day, as I remember, was stubborn. When asked to vacuum the bedroom she did it but I thought there was a real possibility of Beryl (the member of staff) getting the Hoover returned in less than a gentle manner. I had never had a doubt that the move from hospital would be anything but a good one, until then. Shirley accepted what was happening to her, but that was all.

All the clothes we had bought her, she didn't bring any of them with her. We couldn't believe the measly little bag she brought with her from the hospital. Every time we had visited her, we took something from each of us — always a new pair of slippers, a blouse maybe, or a skirt. We never saw them again. What happened to them? None of what she brought with her was what we had bought her. The lovely clothes we bought weren't there. She had on a wool suit which didn't fit very well.

I remember we were hanging curtains with Beryl and the heel came off Beryl's shoe. Shirley's father fixed it. Shirley didn't smile much but I think she settled in well."

There was no immediate prospect of a place for Shirley in the local adult training centre so the opportunities for a changed life style very much centred on the possibilities available in the house and in the town. What is remarkable about Shirley's story is how comprehensively she embraced those possibilities with the support of the staff of the house. Looking back, the course for the future was taking direction even during that first day.

Shirley moved into one of the two double bedrooms in the house, a room which overlooks the front garden and the road which leads to the town centre. The room has a bay window, a washbasin, a fitted carpet, two single divans, two wardrobes, and two chests-of-drawers each with a dressing-table mirror. Shirley unpacked with her sisters' help and arranged her possessions; and in doing so she began her life as an adult with responsibilities, a person who generated household work and therefore could be called upon to contribute to getting it done. The house was not especially arranged for Shirley prior to her arrival. The model was not that of an hotel. During the afternoon she made her own bed, helping to iron the sheets, pillow case, and duvet cover that were needed. She vacuumed her bedroom and the adjacent landing carpet.

The staff had just completed a two-week induction course. There could have been a view that "the work starts tomorrow". But the work of the staff was, and is, to help the adults lead an ordinary life. Those of us who were involved in setting up the house feel, looking back, that the orientation of the staff was built-up in the induction period and was subsequently reinforced and developed without interruption or exception. With a clear emphasis on resident participation it was important to develop staff skill in helping the people moving in to participate. This is a practical skill which can only be achieved through practice and which has its reward in the increased abilities and contribution of the people for whom they are caring. We cannot be absolutely sure that Shirley used a Hoover and an iron literally for the first time in her life that day, but the introduction of new experiences and opportunities to be involved in everyday events can be said to characterise the contribution of the new service, not only for Shirley but for other people who were to live in the house with her.

Some people may think this approach is too task-oriented and lacking in empathy. In our experience the normal warmth and emotion of human interaction is brought out by sharing in the ordinary things of life. It is when these ordinary things are missing, or when a relationship is not one of sharing and reciprocal contribution, that normal social interactions become distorted and mutual respect is lost. Even on the first day, Shirley needed to be occupied. There was a limit to the length of time that Shirley or her family would want to sit with each other unoccupied; the more so because of a virtual inability to converse or communicate by any means. Everything that has happened since indicates that having the opportunity to join in from the start was acceptable and preferable to Shirley.

We had wondered what we would do about Shirley's favourite activity of pushing her doll's pram. Thankfully, the problem did not arise. Domestic activity became her preferred choice from the moment the handle of the vacuum cleaner was placed in her hand. There was no coercion involved. Shirley's pram and dolls were put in her bedroom and were available for her to use. After some months, during which they were never touched, they were put in the attic storeroom; and some months later they were finally discarded. The operational philosophy of the new service emphasises the supplanting of childish pursuits, possessions, and personal appearance by others that are appropriate to adulthood, and, more specifically, those which are within the range typical of other citizens of the same chronological age. But such an approach is effected gradually. It should not involve vetoing long-standing preferences, denying people of what little they have. This service did not start by rejecting the possessions the people had, even where the only feasible use of them might have been detrimental to the desired image for the house and for the adults who lived in it.

Shirley had opportunities to learn to prepare food, to do the washing and ironing, to dust, polish and clean, and to go shopping. She had a chance to initiate activities and make choices. Another immediate change in her life was a considerably increased involvement with her family. Whereas before distance had limited contact to seeing her whole family together approximately once a month, she was able to see various members of her family weekly on a regular basis, with additional incidental contact as it arose. She might meet one of her sisters in town when shopping, for example, or one might call in for coffee if passing the house. They might come as guests to a summer evening barbecue. At first, Shirley's family were her only regular visitors but an adult friend of the family started to visit as well and is now Shirley's friend independently. One day a week all the sisters meet for lunch at their father's house, a mile or so from 10 Summerton Road.

Shirley was clearly pleased with the move and there has never been any doubt that she prefers her new situation. She has never shown any desire to return to the hospital. She arrived at 10 Summerton Road with few possessions and little high quality, presentable clothing. Her hair was not styled. She had no spectacles although she had poor sight. None of these things was a direct result of her mental handicap. Indeed, the extent of her handicap makes the responsibility that others had for arranging things better for her quite unambiguous. To some extent, such shortcomings may be related to the personal poverty which people with mental handicaps often experience, but such deficiencies are largely due to neglect.

Within a fortnight of moving, Shirley had been to the hairdresser's, she had bought new shoes and some new clothes, and staff had made appointments for her with an opthalmologist and an audiologist for assessment of her vision and hearing.

Prescription of spectacles considerably improved her ability to see with her good eye. Total deafness was confirmed by the audiologist, but we had not wished to assume this simply from the fact that she came from hospital without a hearing aid.

Shirley had no means of communication. There was a distinct possibility that her sight might worsen and this made the teaching of a sign language a matter of urgency. Another almost immediate occurrence, therefore, was the involvement of a speech therapist to teach staff the *Makaton vocabulary* (Walker, 1980) and to advise them on how to teach it to Shirley. This was the first move in establishing a multidisciplinary group of professional staff who, with the house staff and relatives, would constitute a programme planning team to consider Shirley's needs. A formal system of individual programme planning (Jenkins *et al.*, 1988) was established for every person with a mental handicap living in the house (and for others living at home in the community) by about the sixth month of operation. IPP meetings are held at six-monthly intervals for each person and are a valuable source of guidance for and review of the care programmes carried out in the intervening time.

The rapid development of skills and a new life style

One of the most immediate visible signs of change in Shirley was her appearance. Photographs taken at the time of her move show a person with an expressionless, limp face and tousled hair, dressed in clean but unflattering clothes, whose gaze, without glasses, was almost vacant. Six months later her appearance was dramatically different. The skin and muscle tone of her face were tighter, she was smiling at the camera, her eyes were focused, her hair styled; more becoming clothing and a little jewellery enhanced the overall appearance. During the period which marks her change in appearance, Shirley also learned to iron clothing, vacuum carpets, dust and polish, wash up, rinse the crockery, dry up, and load and unload the dishwasher. Soon afterwards she learned how to use the washing machine and hang out the washing, how to put ironed clothes in the airing cupboard, and how to make good use of her own chest of drawers and wardrobe. She was taught to be more careful in her dressing, personal cleanliness, and bathing. Teaching has also covered food preparation and cooking and Shirley can now prepare and cook simple meals and snacks by herself.

Gradually, Shirley has developed many of the skills needed by adults tending to household needs of themselves or others. However, certain features of group residential life still act to limit the extent to which her experience can be similar to that of citizens who are not handicapped. Living in a larger group than most people, Shirley does not always have to cook, wash-up, and clean on every occasion. Instead there is a need to take turns. The sequence of life and the opportunity to do things is often determined by staff. It can easily seem that the permission of staff is required to do things, and the role of the people living in the house is to be passive until asked. It is, therefore, remarkable, and a tribute to the way in which staff supported Shirley, that she began to initiate activity herself: noticing when things needed doing, taking on the responsibility of doing them, taking decisions, and making choices. One of the first signs of this development was when Shirley collected the coffee cups from the lounge after the evening meal and took them to the kitchen without being asked. A second example was when she went out to the washing hanging in the garden to see whether it was dry enough to be brought in. Other developments involved exercising some control over her own life, like deciding to make a cup of tea for herself, or helping herself to a biscuit or some fruit between meals. She also began to choose what she ate at mealtimes and to communicate to staff when she had run out of things she needed help to buy, such as perfume or talcum powder. Other examples illustrate her contribution to the general upkeep of the house: emptying the pedal bin and changing the bin liner when required; changing the handtowels in bathroom and toilets when dirty. For people who have had long experience of institutional life, such developments do not just represent the gaining of skills. Taking initiatives, without first receiving a request or asking permission, represents a significant movement towards a normal adult life style. For this to grow, the social environment needs to reinforce emerging personal independence. Staff need to embrace the changing status of the "client". They need to find a way of teaching competence without appearing to punish imperfect attempts at independence. For example, there is the question of how to encourage someone to choose what they eat and at the same time keep a healthy, balanced diet and avoid excess.

Changes in the nature of Shirley's social life are more difficult to gauge. She had moved from a social setting characterised by the presence of a large number of people with strange behaviour, all being left largely to their own devices. She had moved to a smaller setting with a far greater level of structure directed towards encouraging an ordered pattern of life. Smaller rooms allowed greater scope for privacy; but also for collaboration in activity between individuals rather than the entire residential group. This might be expected to offer better opportunities for the development of individual relationships with staff and other people living in the house, as well as more protection from the unwelcome intrusion of others. This, added to the frequent and regular family contact, must provide Shirley with some security in her view of her place in life. Certainly she smiles and laughs; shows affection to the other people living in the house and to members of staff; thanks people for things that they do for her; and recognises changes in others, showing appreciation of their achievements and concern if they are ill or otherwise low. But she has also had aggressive outbursts since moving to the house, sometimes showing annoyance when other adults approach her. Although in a smaller group, Shirley still lives exclusively with other people who are severely or profoundly mentally handicapped; a matter in which she has never been given a choice. Her companions behave at times in apparently aimless, unpurposeful ways. Shirley has always dealt with irritation caused by other people by being aggressive to them. Her hospital notes, covering a thirty-year period, testify to this. She is cut off from the social world by her deafness. Her sign language is still limited. There is, nevertheless, one substantial difference in the small home: a sympathetic and understanding response to her behavioural outbursts, in contrast to the physical restraint and periods of seclusion she experienced in hospital.

A member of the community

Shirley is visited by and visits other people (mainly family) who live in Merton. She is both a consumer and a customer. She goes to a local optician, dentist, and chiropodist. She has a bank account from which she can obtain money by using a card in a cash dispenser. She has begun to become independent outside the house. As someone registered as blind and deaf she has a red and white, striped cane which she carries when going out. At first she was found to be scared of dogs and cats. A programme of controlled and supported exposure to such animals was conducted over many months, so that she could pass them in the street without panic. She then learned to go to the post box to post letters at the end of the road. More recently, Shirley has been given carefully graduated and supervised opportunities to take herself through the streets of town independently.

Shirley's experience of shopping has developed too. Having rarely before left a hospital campus, and having only seen food coming already cooked and prepared from a central hospital kitchen, Shirley had much to learn. There was a long period in which she was shown elementary facts of shopping, like what goods were in what types of packaging; how to take goods from shelves, use a trolley, and queue at a cash desk; how to unpack and repack goods from trolley to cashier's conveyor belt and then into carrier bags; and how to hand money to the cashier and wait for the change. After months of almost daily practice she has grown in competence and experience. Now she is able to leave the staff member at the supermarket door and purchase a number of goods independently. She uses a specially designed shopping list. Staff put the labels of goods she is to buy inside a plastic wallet. Shirley then collects the goods, matching them to the labels she carries with her. She does not know money values yet, so she is given money that will easily cover the final bill. She hands this to the cashier and collects the change (although she is unable to check it). She also shops with staff for her clothing and other personal requirements.

Shirley also makes use of other services, often going for a drink in a pub or café. She sometimes has opportunities to eat out in a pub or restaurant, mainly with staff and other people from the house, but also with her family on occasions. It is very important that staff have the ability to be flexible in their use of the money budgeted for catering. Just like an ordinary family the people at 10 Summerton Road mainly eat at home but, every now and again, finances stretch to going out. Shirley collects her own pension from the Post Office and, having been taught to write her name, uses her own pension book. In the shopping she does for herself, for the house, and in buying presents for her father and sisters, she is fully involved in making choices. She has learned to sign "for me" for purchases she would like to make for herself.

Having a job

A common problem in developing local, community-based

residential services to replace centralised institutions is that the infrastructure for vocational occupation is not equipped to deal with the influx of people who are brought back to their own localities from distant large hospitals. Soon after people moved in to 10 Summerton Road applications were made for places for them at the local adult training centre, but the length of time taken for individuals to be allocated a social worker, for their application and assessment documents to be processed, and for them to move up the waiting list meant that there was no immediate prospect of any day-care provision for them. There was also the question of what was on offer: the "industrial" activity of the main training centre; or the occupational diversion of the special care or special needs units. These relatively small, more highly staffed areas within the training centre catered for people with severe or profound handicaps, their principal activities comprising training in basic personal and self-help skills, and early cognitive, language, and manipulative abilities. The training materials used are much the same as those used with pre-school or infant children and, although training might be a stated objective, much time is spent using the materials in ways that have long since been learned.

There was a considerable conflict of philosophies here and a problem in deciding what would represent Shirley's best interests. On the one hand, it seemed correct that Shirley (and others in her position) should have the chance to go out during the day and follow some worthwhile occupation. She would gain an increased range of activity, expand her social network, and not be confined to the world of family and the other adults and staff of the house. On the other hand, in the absence of a day-care place she had developed a strongly adult life style involving housework, shopping, and use of community amenities. The opportunity to join a special care/needs group did not seem an attractive or progressive alternative. Even the standard of the main training centre caused concern: the relative lack of intensity of activity; the low level of demand made of the people who were considered to be most handicapped; and the lack of support for individual development. Further, this large, segregated setting had some disadvantages similar to those of the residential service Shirley had only recently left.

Shirley was considered by training centre staff as being in the "grey area" between the more school-oriented special needs unit and the main "work" area. On first application she was said to require special care. However, by the time a place was finally available, opinion had been swayed by the reports of the progress she had made. She was offered a trial period within the main centre. Reservations were expressed over her history of disruptiveness, her lack of communication, and her deafness. These were realistic concerns because of the extremely low staff:trainee ratio within the workshop and the known difficulties for introducing and integrating new trainees to the particular tasks and general routine of the setting. At the same time, staff at the house had been discussing the possibility of finding Shirley an independent job based on her capability in domestic work. They did not know whether this was realistic, but they knew they had the capacity to support her in a job were they able to get one for her because at that time the house was not fully occupied.

With no great hope of immediate success, staff began to inquire about domestic work available locally. Surprisingly, a part-time job was quickly secured on a three-month trial in a firm which contracted to clean office blocks at the end of the working day. At the same time a place in the adult training centre also became available. As an insurance against the job not working out, Shirley began attending the training centre as well as starting her job, but only part-time so that she would not be absolutely exhausted by moving from a situation with no work to one which involved even longer hours than usual. In the event, the training centre place fell through first: on her first day Shirley had an aggressive outburst which staff felt was beyond their management. The possibility of exclusion was raised. House staff decided to take pre-emptive action. They withdrew Shirley from the training centre voluntarily to avoid an official decision being made against her: still being uncertain whether her employment would be sustained they wanted to retain the possibility of re-securing a training centre place if necessary.

Over the next two months Shirley went to work in the early evening with a member of staff, whose role was to teach her the job routine and, at first, to make good any shortfall in her standard of work by acting as a co-worker, helping to do the job directly. Shirley made substantial progress in learning the required sequence and thoroughness of the job. Direct staff help lessened and the firm supervisor was pleased with the arrangement. However, near the end of the trial period she had one bad day; an aggressive outburst occurred at work during which Shirley ripped some posters and papers from an office wall. This alarmed other members of the work force and employees of the firm whose offices were being cleaned, as well as causing actual damage. Staff made good the damage as far as was possible and her employer was sympathetic to the incident. However, Shirley lost the job. The house staff were not dismayed. In discussion afterwards, staff thought the job Shirley had been given was particularly exacting. On one occasion when Shirley had been ill, a member of staff had done her job in her place in order to avoid jeopardising the trial. She found it involved continuous hard work to complete the assignment, harder it seemed than was required of others on the contract. They decided not to appeal against the decision but to find Shirley a better job.

Shirley's next job involved cleaning a public house before opening two mornings a week. Again staff support was provided to ensure Shirley's safe travel across town to the job, to teach her the specific requirements and, at first, to give direct help. During the following year, two developments occurred. As Shirley became more proficient, the staff role reduced to that of escort for the journeys to and from work only. Secondly, as other domestic employees left the pub, Shirley was given their jobs also, building up to her working for two hours every week-day morning. She earns the proper adult wage for the job and has been re-employed now through three changes in landlord. At first staff had agreed to cover any absence due to sickness by doing the job themselves, but after about a year, her contract was renegotiated to remove this arrangement. Staff support is now limited. For a while it ceased completely because a volunteer acted as escort, but now Shirley is being taught to make the journey independently and staff input is needed for this. It is likely that staff support will need to be reintroduced from time to time. Periodically, especially with a change in the management of the pub, Shirley's job is redefined; a different order of cleaning, or a change in the areas to be cleaned, is introduced. When this happens, because her deafness and limited use of sign language make communication of change difficult, staff are responsible for helping her adapt to the new requirements. The method of teaching is essentially habit training; while Shirley is in the process of learning the new routine, staff presence is required.

Recently a researcher, interested in looking at people with

mental handicaps in competitive employment nationally, accompanied Shirley to work in order to describe her situation. The following is abstracted from her account:

"I visited on two occasions. On my first visit, Shirley was in bed with 'flu and could not go to work, a very rare occurrence. I did not meet her, but had a chance to talk to the person in charge of the house about her background and the job. On my second visit I was able to accompany Shirley and Rosa, a member of staff, to the pub, where I watched Shirley work, and talked to the landlord, John.

On my second visit, I arrived at the house at about 9.00 am. Shirley was washing up the breakfast dishes. Before we left, she made us a cup of coffee which we drank in the lounge. Although she has no speech, we communicated with smiles and a little Makaton.

Soon she seemed to realise that it was time to go and, without reminder, went upstairs to get her coat, walking stick, and dusting cloths. Shirley, Rosa, and I walked through the town centre to get to the pub. Shirley pushed the button at the road crossings but it was difficult to tell whether she could see the 'green man' or traffic.

When we arrived at the pub, John was busy talking to a delivery man. Shirley went straight in, took off her coat, and got to work. She had been taught the job sequence and how to do each task by staff of the house. This careful teaching had taken about six months plus two months of 'fine tuning', but Shirley now knows the routine and works very independently. Shirley washed all the tables, chairs, and surfaces, vacuumed the carpets, cleaned the toilets, washed the floors, polished the tables, chairs, and bar, and put beer mats and ash trays on the tables. She worked very quickly and with no reminder of the next task. Rosa occasionally pointed out a corner that she'd missed because of her sight. While Shirley worked I took photographs, after asking her permission by showing her the camera and getting her nodded agreement. After I'd taken a few, Shirley came to get me when she started a new task, pointing to the camera and obviously posing.

While she was working I also had the opportunity to interview John who was accompanied by his three-year old son, Thomas. John is not the real landlord, but he and his partner own a small brewery, and this and another pub. John is filling in while waiting for a newly employed landlord to take over. Another landlord initially employed Shirley although John was aware of her employment and has known her since she started work at the pub.

John said that at first Shirley wasn't paid for her work and she had been taken on to get a little free cleaning and also to help her out. (Staff later told me that John may not have realised that she was paid at first.) Later, when she was employed as the cleaner it was definitely on merit. John said she cleans the pub very well: 'The pub gets a good going over. It's much cleaner than the average pub'. John reported that there were still occasionally times when Shirley would get upset and perhaps break her spectacles. Once she broke an ash tray, but these (occurrences) were very rare and not of concern to him. There had been a time in the early days when she'd pulled the hair of the young daughter of the previous landlord but the family was very understanding and neither they nor the little girl had been overly upset by the incident.

John said he felt there were many benefits in employing Shirley. He had seen her develop and gain confidence: 'I can tell when she's enjoying herself, she's a good worker'. He also felt that he and his family had benefited from knowing Shirley and that his four children seemed to have gained insight into other people's handicaps by knowing her. The regular customers know Shirley and many have commented that they think it's very good to have Shirley working there.

When Shirley finished cleaning she put on her coat, gathered up her materials, and came to John for her pay, which she gets each day. She has recently been learning to write her name so that she can sign for her money. Shirley signed her name and John gave her the thumbs up sign and said "good". Shirley smiled brightly, gave him the thumbs up sign and waved good-bye. John said, 'She doesn't like to hang about. She likes to get on with things'.

As we walked back to the house, Rosa said they often stop in town for coffee or to do a bit of shopping but today they needed to get back because, on Thursday, Shirley goes to her father's home for lunch with her sisters. Shirley has recently purchased new curtains for her room with money she's saved from her earnings and is also saving for a holiday.

Watching Shirley clean the pub, get her pay, and walk cheerfully home to meet her sisters for lunch, I couldn't help thinking of her previous life pushing a doll's pram around the hospital grounds day after day. The fact that Shirley has a job is certainly a credit to the staff of the house who persevered against what would seem to most people to be insurmountable odds. It is also in large part due to the pub landlord who was willing to give Shirley a chance to show what she could do.

But the real achievement has been made by Shirley, who with the opportunity, help, and support, is doing a real job and getting paid for it."

(Taken from Porterfield and Gathercole, 1985.)

Disruptive behaviour: a person from a "locked" ward

Anyone meeting Shirley now would find it difficult to believe that the person busy at work or helping to run the house, herself small in stature, should ever have been considered someone whose problem was defined primarily in terms of behavioural disturbance. Yet she had lived for thirty years in a hospital ward specially designated for such people. When the feasibility of community living is debated it is often people in secure institutional environments who are cited as those who cannot be cared for in ordinary domestic houses. Three people described in this book came to 10 Summerton Road from locked facilities. So what sort of challenge did their behaviour present? In this section we explore this question in relation to Shirley. What was it she actually did? How was it interpreted in the hospital? What was the hospital staff response to it? How was it interpreted differently in Summerton Road? What was the response of the staff there?

Throughout most of Shirley's life, periodic outbursts of severe, aggressive behaviour have been part of the picture. The majority of her hospital notes and any planned treatment she received in hospital was related to her aggression. There were regular entries in her psychiatric notes which recorded continuing disturbed behaviour. She was prescribed major tranquillisers and hypnotics to be administered daily. She was also prescribed more powerful doses of similar drugs, to be used at the discretion of nursing staff, to sedate her after a severe outburst. In her notes were about six "incident forms" per year describing attacks Shirley had made on other people. These forms also described strategies staff had adopted for dealing with the attacks, which included secluding Shirley in a side room and dressing her in restraining clothing. There were also a number of casualty notices which recorded injuries Shirley had either received from the attacks of others or inflicted on herself. The night report book from the ward frequently recorded attacks on other people in the dormitory, which involved Shirley turning them out of bed. Both the pattern of behaviour and the type of treatment given by staff were evident way back into her childhood and throughout the three-and-a-half decades Shirley spent in the hospital.

There was little evidence of any attempt to understand her aggression other than by a psychiatric explanation; that is, her attacks were crazy, senseless, a symptom of her being deranged. Her medication was the same as that given for acute and chronic schizophrenia and maintenance of psycho-sedation in people with major psychoses. The fact that the frequency and content of her outbursts and the recorded comments about her remained similar over more than thirty years showed the treatment and continual adjustment of medication did not eliminate the pattern of behaviour. Rather than looking to a questioning of the psychiatric assessment, the records seem only to have confirmed the underlying diagnosis. Other possibilities had been hinted at but never followed through to the point of affecting what happened to Shirley. A relatively recent nursing note had suggested a possible association between her outbursts and her menstrual cycle. In the last year of her stay in the hospital, prompted by a change in Shirley's consultant psychiatrist, a referral for a psychological opinion was made. The psychologist was concerned about her lack of occupation and suggested enrolment in the adult education activities and sign language classes within the hospital. An improvement in general spirits at that time and a concomitant reduction in disruptive behaviour were attributed to Shirley having a new doll's pram to push around the hospital grounds. In terms of length of report, this appeared to be the most thorough and coordinated attempt to understand why Shirley might choose to attack others and inflict injury on herself. Unfortunately, no action was taken to increase the range of activities available to her.

After moving to 10 Summerton Road, Shirley's disruptiveness reduced dramatically. A number of inappropriate but mild attacks on others did occur (simple pushes or slaps) which seemed to be a method of communicating her annoyance at their intrusion and a signal to be left alone. Typically, Shirley would be moved from the situation and staff would show disapproval. She always seemed sorry for her actions. Then, after what appeared to have been a "honeymoon" period in the home of about six months, during which Shirley was very happy and showed no sign of major disruption, a number of more severe incidents took place which followed the same kind of periodic occurrence as before.

Outbursts were of the following types: self-injury of the face around the eyes, which usually broke her spectacles, often coupled with an extreme state of excited anxiety which resulted in damage to the physical surroundings (for example, tearing the poster from the office wall at work, throwing a plate, hitting the wall with her fist); pulling the hair of nearby staff or other adults living in the house in an unprovoked attack; and, on about two occasions in as many years, tipping the person sharing her bedroom out of bed. Again, afterwards Shirley showed every sign of being sorry for what she had done.

These outbursts were quite sudden. Staff naturally reacted with surprise and sought to protect other people living in the house and their own well-being. In this they displayed signs of disapproval, while also seeking to calm Shirley, holding her hands down, removing her from the situation, and telling her to stop. These measures were quite sufficient. Since moving to the house, it has never been necessary for Shirley to experience sedation, the use of restraining clothing, or seclusion.

Despite the impression that might have been gained from her recorded history and disruptive status, Shirley's disturbed behaviour has never been so extensive as to constitute a serious problem of day-to-day management. Nor, in contrast to much that is suggested about people with mental handicaps, was it ever viewed as an impediment to her living in the community. Whether Shirley could or should continue to live at 10 Summerton Road was never at issue. However, the attacks, particularly given their re-emergence after a tranquil period, were taken very seriously indeed. It was very important to understand them and prevent them recurring if it was at all possible. Shirley's self-injury could jeopardise her already limited eyesight, and in practical terms it was expensive in repair or replacement of broken spectacles. Her attacks on others, as well as being mildly injurious at the time, interfered with a healthy growth of relationships and trust. Attacks on staff also had the potential of being severely detrimental to working relationships but, in fact, never proved to be.

In order to try to find the basic cause of the outbursts a record of incidents was kept and compared to Shirley's menstrual cycle. At the same time, an attempt was made to analyse whether there were conspicuous environmental precursors or consequences that may generate the behaviour. For the major outbursts none could be found; and the tie to the menstrual cycle was only partially convincing. Staff did notice that prior to an outburst, Shirley seemed to show signs of discomfort; either rubbing her stomach, or feeling her brow, or both. Shirley's deafness and lack of sign language still enforce on her a substantial degree of isolation and, although she continues to learn signs and use them expressively, acquisition takes time; added to this abstract notions are much more difficult to teach than comparatively simple labelling of objects and actions. One possibility was that her aggression was associated with being in pain, something which she had no means to tell anyone about. It seemed quite reasonable to assume that pain might provide a setting condition for outbursts of irritability that could take the forms described. The consequence of her aggression in the past had been seclusion or restraint. Both imply removal from a possible source of irritation, the absence of demand, and the opportunity to rest. Sedation guarantees this. It is not beyond belief that the treatment she received in hospital reinforced her aggressive behaviour.

This analysis also helped to explain the periodic but variable relationship of outbursts to her menstrual cycle. If Shirley suffered from pre-menstrual tension, there would be a tendency for periodic recurrence of pain. It may not always be so acute that Shirley would be unable to contain her distress and thus the relationship may not be consistently observed. Moreover, other sources of pain (mild illness, headache) could cause distress at times unrelated to the menstrual cycle. Enduring shifts in base-level mood, such as may have been caused by the acquisition of a new pram or the move to 10 Summerton Road, may also have changed the likelihood of an extreme demonstration of irritability.

We were in the position of trying to make a reasonable picture out of a number of seemingly relevant observations. We could have been entirely wrong, but staff thought it was worth following this direction a little further to see what a treatment programme based on this interpretation might be. It appeared to have two dimensions. One was to try to prevent the pain early in its onset. In the final analysis, however, this could only be reliably detected by Shirley herself and she was unable to tell us about it. Therefore a second dimension was to teach Shirley an alternative response to aggression in order to communicate distress and gain relief. The absence of an ability to communicate directly with Shirley, coupled with the low frequency of occurrence of the problem, meant that staff had to be patient and seek a long-term re-education process. It was decided to try the following. The problem of tipping people out of bed at night could be remedied by Shirley having her own bedroom. Carol, who had initially been given a single room, had developed some interests in common with Kathleen, who had only recently moved to the house. They began to share a room and Shirley moved to the vacated single room, a move which pleased her. Secondly, Shirley was given a course of prophylactic medication in the middle of her menstrual cycle designed to regulate and ease any pre-menstrual tension. Thirdly, a programme of teaching Shirley to look after and take mild analgesics herself when needed was started. In addition she was given regular opportunities to rest, without having to resort to prior aggression. Lastly the signing of discomfort by rubbing her stomach or temple was encouraged and the *Makaton* sign for "pill" was taught.

Disruptions are now much reduced in frequency and severity. Staff still have some difficulty in deciding when Shirley is sufficiently off-colour not to go to work or when they should encourage her to be less active in the house. So much of her activity is self-initiated these days that it is a matter of encouraging her to put her feet up. If she lived with less people, or with people who were not handicapped, the few outbursts which do still occur may not happen. There has been one incident at the pub, which may have been due to her working while ill, but her current employers appear to accept that this may occasionally happen. Staff in the house also accept there may be the odd incident. Basically such events are shrugged off. Shirley is no longer defined by a behavioural manifestation which occurs infrequently, lasts only a short time, and ends without the need for intervention.

Three years on

Three years after moving from the hospital where she had lived since the age of six, Shirley is living in a comfortable, well-furnished house in a pleasant town, with a regular part-time job and close involvement with her family. Given the philosophies to which staff of the house adhere — the importance of participation, development, and the treating of people who have reached the age of majority as adults irrespective of their level of handicap — Shirley is able to make choices which concern her welfare, initiate activity on her own and on others' behalf, and take on adult responsibilities. Her life has an adult routine which she has adopted without the benefit of language. She appears to know the time of day and the days of the week. She gets up and prepares for work Monday to Friday, but takes a more leisurely view of things at week-ends. She anticipates mealtimes, changes in staff shifts, and her relatives' regular contact. Like other people who work, Shirley takes holidays; some of which she spends at home and others on vacation (with staff and one of the other women). Again, like other people who work and who have household responsibilities, she has a meaningful sense of leisure; gardening, watering the indoor plants, and watching television are hobbies rather than "occupation" or "therapy".

Despite all of this it is still clear that there are limitations to her freedom and development which are inherent in living with a group of other adults with severe or profound mental handicaps. These are brought about partly by living in a social world defined by skill deficiency and partly through the simple need to conform to the order of a group routine.

Gaining a job provided an important complementary emphasis to the development of a different way of life for Shirley, which followed moving out of hospital. In this respect, Shirley has achieved more than the other people living in the house (and more than most people with mental handicaps who attend adult training centres). She has achieved the status of an employee, paid at parity with other citizens who have no disabilities who undertake similar employment. But not only that, she is doing something which is entirely individual to her. Part of her life is arranged with just her in mind and for her own benefit. There are demands which she has to meet independently of the people who share the house with her and under her own steam. In contrast, the adults who go to the day-care service from the house do so as a group. They used to go in organised transport, all at the same time, although Carol now makes her way independently on public transport. But the similarity and sharing of demands means that those going to the day service provide cues for each other and the staff routine is determined by their needs as a group. There is a collective responsibility and in this each individual escapes a certain amount of personal responsibility.

Gainful employment has also meant that Shirley has an income of her own which has obvious benefits. One is that she can begin to afford some of the things which help adults meet their commitments and responsibilities. Monday to Friday she needs to get up in time to go to work. She has an alarm clock to wake her; one which she can place under her pillow and which signals by vibration. She has an automatic tea-maker in her room to help her start the day. Out of her own pocket, Shirley has also been able to refurnish her room, redecorate, and replace the curtains and some linen.

Having an income also led to a consideration of how to teach Shirley to use a bank. Given her language difficulties and her late start in learning any form of communication, we decided that it was unrealistic to expect her to learn to read or write. The writing of cheques was not considered a possibility. However, we are now in the age of the computer and the cash card economy; more gets done simply by pushing buttons. Shirley had some understanding of number. For example, she would usually lay the correct number of places at the lunch table even though the number of people taking lunch would vary from day to day. To enhance this ability, a formal programme of matching quantities to numerals was undertaken. Her success indicated an obvious ability to discriminate numerals: this was taken as a starting point for teaching her to use the bank's cash dispensing machine. The target set was to teach Shirley how to push the sequence of buttons to enter her personal code in the machine. As such machines have a safety device of confiscating the user's card if consecutive errors are made in the keying in of a personal number, the teaching was conducted initially on a desk-top calculator which had a key configuration similar to that of the cash dispenser. This had the added advantage of giving visual feedback on the correctness of keying to the model. Once Shirley succeeded in this she progressed to using the proper machine and was given further instruction on the other steps involved. An earlier programme had already taught her to sign her name. Shirley can now sign for her wages, sign her paying-in-slip when banking them, and get her money out of the bank when she needs it.

Shirley's inability to communicate is still a major difficulty. Her knowledge of signing is increasing. She currently uses most of the signs in the first two levels of the *Makaton Vocabulary* (Walker, 1980) which are relevant to her life, as well as other interpretable gestures. She has both expressive and receptive abilities in this respect, but the joys of conversation are still not available to her. Shirley's clothing and grooming is better than when in hospital;

she dresses smartly, appropriate to her age. She is presentable and stylish. This is attributable partly to income, partly to a wider range of choice that the shops in the local town and neighbouring cities offer, and partly to her clothes being better laundered and, if necessary, dry cleaned. At root it also reflects a staff and service orientation that these things are important and cannot be neglected with an easy conscience. Blame cannot be transferred to the handicap of the person suffering the neglect.

Considerable change has been accomplished. Already Shirley has developed so much in a few years that the question of a move towards further independence must be considered; a placement which will provide her with greater opportunity but still within a supportive structure. The change we have seen has often belied the formerly consistent assessment of Shirley as a person in the lower range of the category "severely mentally handicapped". Perhaps because her deafness made accurate assessment difficult it is possible that her intellectual impairment may not be as great as test results suggested. In a developmental assessment we conducted as part of our research at the time of her move, Shirley had no measurable ability in hearing and speech. She passed items concerned with eye/hand coordination and manipulative performance to the level of normal three-year-old development, and some of her locomotor and personal skills were typical of six-year-olds. As a woman in her forties, there was no question that she was severely delayed. Moreover, in terms of her life style, the experiences that she has had, and the progress she has made, a reappraisal of the precise severity of mental handicap after the event is somewhat academic.

It is important to realise that not everyone considered severely mentally handicapped moving from a large hospital will develop as dramatically as Shirley; but the fact remains that some may. Shirley is unlikely to be the sole example. It is only since moving to the greater opportunities of the small house with the developmental orientation of its staff, that any doubt over the severity of Shirley's handicap has arisen. For thirty-five years professionals were happy in their assessment. However long she had stayed in hospital, would anything have happened to cause any doubt? Could the organisation have been changed to give the same kind of supported opportunity and careful planning? Would Shirley ever even have acquired a pair of spectacles? It is hard to imagine the first two questions being answered in the affirmative.

And even if some "radical improvement" to the institutional organisation had secured the provision of spectacles, would it have managed to replace them every time they were broken by Shirley, by accident, or by another resident?

The other defining characteristic of Shirley's previous situation was her status as a disruptive person. The objective description of her even shortly before her move hardly conveys the picture of challenge which people imagine when discussing whether there are people in the long-stay institutions for whom community care is not a realistic possibility. But someone must have considered her to have presented a serious problem for her to have been resident not just in hospital but in a locked ward within that hospital for so long. We cannot have it both ways. We cannot maintain that the institutional system is necessary and that people who live under more secure arrangements do so because of genuine difficulties of management, and at the same time suggest that people who flourish after leaving such an environment were not really difficult anyway. Either there are fewer people living in the existing institutions who are likely to present severe challenges elsewhere than is often stated; or the stated number of people do exist but their behaviour can change dramatically given new and improved surroundings. Both these alternatives give ground for optimism, providing the orientation and care of the staff at 10 Summerton Road can be replicated in other similar settings.

REFERENCES

Jenkins, J., Felce, D., Toogood, S., Mansell, J., de Kock, U. *Individual Programme Planning*. Kidderminster: BIMH Publications, 1988.

Porterfield, J., Gathercole, C. *The Employment of People with Mental Handicap: progress towards an ordinary working life. Looking at people working*. London: King's Fund, 1985.

Walker, M. *The Revised Makaton Vocabulary*. Camberley: Makaton Vocabulary Development Project, 1980.

CHAPTER 3

Catherine Henderson — avoiding institutional care

Catherine Henderson arrived at 10 Summerton Road on the same day as Shirley White, three weeks before her twenty-second birthday. Unlike Shirley, she came from her family home nearby and was already known to the local neighbourhood. She has a profound mental handicap, with very limited ability and, on arrival, seemingly little inclination to respond to the requests of others. Her parents were in quite desperate straits: Catherine wandered constantly and could not be controlled verbally. Their entire day was geared to coping with her as best they could, a task which was placing a considerable strain on them.

We first met Catherine's parents at a meeting for members of a local voluntary society whom we consulted regularly over the provision of the house. Discussions were often difficult; society members wanting to have some control over who was to be admitted and disagreeing strongly with our view of an arbitrary admission policy based on catchment area. Quite understandably from their point of view, the wish that Catherine should be guaranteed one of the first available places was one objective behind the lengthy discussion of the issue. From our viewpoint, however, the service needed a responsible policy to ensure equal opportunity for any eligible person with a mental handicap. The debate on principle was never actually resolved.

In the event, Catherine gained a place at 10 Summerton Road by virtue of her residence in its designated catchment area. She and her family were clearly in need of a high quality, competent service. Discussions gave us a vivid insight into the family situation, the strains being experienced, and the grave possibility of imminent breakdown. As will become clear, Catherine's behaviour posed constant problems of management, and she had few redeeming skills to provide balance between stress and hard work on the one hand and enjoyment on the other.

Catherine, unlike many people with similar behavioural and intellectual characteristics, was not already in residential care because her parents had fought against her placement in an institution. That was the last thing they wanted for their daughter.

They had accepted short-term placements in the two nearest large mental handicap hospitals but had been distressed about her condition on her return home. During her last short-term placement Catherine had been transferred to the locked ward where Shirley had lived. Pressure on her parents meant that they had to accept whatever short-term respite was offered but they were aided in their resolve not to accept long-term care in an institution by the views and support of some of the prominent members of the local voluntary society. These members counselled against accepting long-term institutional admission and actively campaigned for community-based alternatives to be developed. They had raised the capital required for a local hostel which had been given to the social services department some three years earlier. It was a considerable disappointment to Catherine's parents that people as severely handicapped as their daughter could not be considered for admission there. They continued to care for Catherine as best they could, whilst hoping for further local developments and an improvement in the quality of residential services.

The opening of 10 Summerton Road was, therefore, what Catherine's parents had always hoped and waited for. They had no doubt that they wanted Catherine to leave home when the house was ready. Although she had a place in the special care unit of the local adult training centre, the break provided to her parents was insufficient to alleviate the strain. Catherine was supposed to arrive after the others and be collected earlier, staying between 10.00 am and 3.15 pm approximately. Her mother used to try to delay the time she arrived to pick her up in the afternoon as much as possible. From then on it was home, tea, an attempt at containment, and off to bed in the early evening. Of course an adult cannot sleep for more than twelve hours every night and so Catherine learned to rise early — anything from 5.00 am onwards. At least one of her parents had to get up and stay with her, often resorting to driving her around in the car as a means of occupation and distraction until the time permitted for her to arrive at the training centre.

Catherine, having a profound handicap, had very few positive skills and little means of occupying her time. She had a few poorly articulated words, mainly the names of people and foods. She was ambulant, overweight, and wandered with a rocking gait. She pestered for food, would help herself to it, and would not stop when told "no". She ate very noisily, using a spoon and fingers and leaning well over the table so that her mouth was close to the level of the plate. She did not help with dressing or washing, was doubly incontinent at night, and had accidents during the day. Some of these "accidents" may have been deliberate. Her most conspicious characteristic was persistent removal of her clothing. This had been a problem behaviour for many years. One of us had even been asked to advise staff in the special care unit about it (obviously unsuccessfully) some five years before.

When Catherine moved to 10 Summerton Road, she was in the habit of removing her clothing continuously throughout the day. Every attempt to get her clothes back on was met by almost immediate, if not simultaneous, undressing. Consequently, she spent as much as seven hours of her day in a state of partial or complete undress. There was no time during the day when it could be guaranteed that Catherine would not strip, irrespective of where she was. It was not unusual to walk into the room at the special care unit and find her naked, sitting on a chair with a blanket draped across her. The frustration felt by staff was made worse on occasions if, having managed to dress her completely, she then wet herself causing them to undress her again to wash her and change her clothes.

On coming to the house, Catherine's wardrobe comprised an outdoor coat, socks, pants, sandals, and a number of blue towelling one-piece catsuits which tied at the back with four bows. Catherine liked blue; it was the only colour she would allow people to dress her in. The one-piece suits were an attempt to discourage her from stripping. After a period of short-term care in one of the mental handicap hospitals, Catherine had been returned home in a nylon "strong-suit"; a sturdy, one-piece garment resistant to removal or destruction. This was seen as being too severe but it contained the germ of a good idea. Catherine's parents asked one of the members of staff of the special care unit to make up some equivalents from blue towelling. Unfortunately, these were not very helpful in controlling stripping because Catherine could remove them. Unlike nylon, the towelling could be pulled out of shape and the ties weakened. However, irrespective of this, the blue suits became an important element of Catherine's management strategy. Despite their unsightliness they were accepted as her only form of attire during the first few months at the house.

Catherine was very heavy, weighing about fourteen stones. Coupled with her poor gait, this meant that she could only walk a short distance by herself. She was in receipt of Mobility Allowance and she possessed a wheelchair which her parents had used when taking her shopping. The hair on her head was thin, she had more facial hair than usual for a young woman, and she drooled at the mouth, making an almost constant wet area on the front of her clothing. As with Shirley originally, the severity of Catherine's handicap was made noticeable to all, and even accentuated, by her appearance.

Initial management

Of the people who were moving to 10 Summerton Road in the first months, Catherine presented the most conspicuous and constant picture of difficulty. Her behaviour, though harmless, was highly detrimental, time-consuming, and inappropriate. She had a profound mental handicap, few self-help skills, virtually no form of constructive occupation, an inability to sit (except at mealtimes) for anything longer than literally a few seconds, and an absence of response to requests, even to the point of failing to give any indication that she was aware that she had been addressed. She took no notice of people when they initiated contact; and did not make eye-contact with them (that is, look at their eyes when they talked to her) even when they were directly in front of her. However, she was not in herself unsociable. She liked company, and if she had any wants she would approach people to make demands. Under these circumstances she established good eye-contact! But she had no interest in meeting the demands others might have of her. It was part of her lack of skill. Instead she wandered ceaselessly, performing a characteristic, ritual movement which involved holding her left arm up, one finger pointing forward, and rotating it in circular fashion in the left-hand side of her field of vision.

Apart from helping Catherine to settle into her new home, initial service effort followed three complementary strategies: a systematic programme of staff response to stripping, with a view to Catherine choosing to remain dressed throughout the day; staff concentration on finding a means of occupying Catherine more constructively to fill the time she spent wandering or stripping; and, provision of help to improve her physical appearance, including weight reduction, change to conventional clothing, better hairstyling, and control of drooling.

The three priority areas were interrelated: a major loss of weight and an end to the use of the blue suits would require a completely new wardrobe. They needed to be done in concert because money for new clothes was limited. It was also thought that the transfer to conventional clothing should follow successful management of stripping; the first target for remaining dressed being for Catherine to keep on the blue suits. While proceeding with the weight reduction other ways of improving Catherine's appearance were sought, such as having her hair smartly cut and excessive facial hair removed. It was also important for staff to have a coherent approach to occupying her when up and dressed. A fairly crude initial appraisal was that the stripping acted as a non-verbal form of communication which solicited, and usually gained, staff attention. Reversal of the inclination to strip, therefore, depended firstly on Catherine discovering that she would lose staff attention through being naked and could only regain it by dressing. But secondly, and perhaps equally importantly in the longer term, it depended on Catherine gaining staff attention for doing other, more constructive, things. Thus, staff had to help her with constructive activities. As Catherine is profoundly mentally handicapped, staff help needed to be extensive. Given Catherine's slowness in learning, her participation in constructive activities could not wait for her to be taught new skills. The strategy had to be that she would be immediately involved in the activities of the house with whatever staff support was required to bridge the gap between her capabilities and the requirements of the task.

During the initial period after opening, only four people with mental handicaps lived in the house and although a full complement of staff had not been appointed, the staff:resident ratio was at its highest during this critical period. Catherine was almost constantly with a member of staff. The easy part of the strategy was the diet. A one thousand calories per day reducing diet was designed following consultation with a dietician. But the approach to stripping and to getting Catherine to participate in constructive activities were full-time, day-long endeavours.

The initial programme to reduce stripping was as follows. It was decided that Catherine could choose to be naked if she wished but, if she did so, she must obey the normal convention of decency and stay in the privacy of her own room. (She had a single bedroom upstairs.) If she stripped elsewhere in the house, staff would take her and her clothes to her bedroom and wait outside for her on the landing. When she wanted to leave her room and rejoin the activities of the house, she would be given the opportunity to dress and helped to do so. If she did not dress she stayed in her room. When dressed, staff would re-engage Catherine in the life of the house, joining in ordinary household and self-care activities. To achieve this often called for complete physical guidance, a staff member's hands over Catherine's helping her to do the task. Moreover, an arm would often need to be around her waist to prevent her from wandering away. Also, at this stage Catherine did not always look at what she was doing which of course did not help her to make a positive contribution to the activity. There was, however, no obvious alternative to this strategy of maximum help if Catherine were ever to become engaged in useful activity for which she could gain considerable staff attention.

This approach to stripping was rapidly effective in altering the balance of Catherine's day. In the first five days of November she spent over twenty-three hours in the house undressed. In the first five days of December, January, and February she spent two, six and five hours respectively in a state of undress. Attempts to strip still occurred, however, so management of the behaviour still occupied a considerable amount of staff time. In order for the approach to be effective, a member of staff had to remain by Catherine's bedroom door, ready to offer her the opportunity to dress when she wanted to return to the household and to prevent her from doing so undressed. The approach was, in essence, a "time-out" procedure in which Catherine spent periods of time away from any possibility of gaining staff attention. She regained attention immediately upon dressing and continued to have the opportunity of attention as long as she remained dressed.

Although clearly effective, operating a "time-out" procedure such as this puts pressures on staff. For staff in this instance the procedure involved many occasions of boredom, waiting outside Catherine's bedroom door until she chose to rejoin the activity of the house. There was a temptation to avoid this boring wait by preventing Catherine from taking off her clothes in the first place. Staff had by now become proficient at getting Catherine to dress in the morning and after episodes of stripping. They were also better at intervening to prevent stripping, *but this strategy had to be avoided* as it represented a return to the habitual way of responding to the first signs of stripping by providing Catherine with immediate staff attention. If staff did successfully intervene to dissuade Catherine from continuing to strip, not only was Catherine rewarded by gaining their attention but staff too were rewarded for avoiding the time-consuming management procedure. Prevention, therefore, was a tempting option. Even when they did try, staff could not always prevent Catherine from stripping. There were occasions when, if she wanted to continue to undress despite their attempts to prevent her, she would drop to the floor to counter staff correction. Being strong and fairly heavy she could usually remove some clothing whenever she wanted.

Prevention of Catherine's stripping had to be vetoed. The emphasis had to be on allowing her to take clothes off unconstrained and then to remove her from any situation in which she could gain attention. This approach had to be strictly established if Catherine was to learn that the consequences her behaviour brought had changed; that people were no longer going to respond in the way she predicted and desired. To emphasise this the function of stripping was defined and made known to everyone in contact with her: *Catherine was not stripping in order to be naked but in order for staff (or parents) to stop her, thus providing her with attention*. Everyone, therefore, must try not to attempt to stop her and must interact with her only when she began to get dressed again and for as long as she remained clothed.

By and large this emphasis was well-maintained. The frequency with which Catherine removed her clothing soon became relatively low. Even so, the approach was still time-consuming when Catherine chose to spend a long time in her bedroom before signalling her desire to rejoin the activities of the house. By this time Catherine was less heavy as a result of her diet, she was easier to work with, staff had become better at getting her to dress, and she herself was becoming more cooperative. In view of this the programme was modified to cut down the time it took. Catherine was taken to her room on stripping as before, but after a defined time staff would enter the room and dress her. The immediate consequence of this was that she spent less time in her room and more time involved in the life of the house. At this stage there were increasingly whole days spent without any attempt to strip.

While this was happening, the careful diet was having dramatic results. Catherine's weight reduced from fourteen stones to eight-and-a-half stones; from a dress size 20 to size 10. She has remained about this weight ever since, moving up to size 12 and maintaining that size. Her skin and muscle tone were very loose after such a large loss in weight but these have tightened with time. Catherine's reduction in size greatly increased the potential for an overall improvement in appearance. The prospect was still marred by the continuing use of the blue suits, which were now not only stretched and worn through repeated attempts to strip but also voluminous. As Catherine had reached her target weight and was keeping the blue suits on for longer periods without stripping, it was considered that the time was right for a change to conventional clothing. This was achieved during the two-week summer closure of the day centre, seven months after Catherine came to live at 10 Summerton Road. Before moving on, however, another part of the story of her first six months at the house will be described.

Catherine's weight loss had other important consequences. The orientation of the house included developing a life in the community which was as full as it could be, given the limiting handicaps of the people living in it, and wherever possible to use the normal social means to achieve it. Going shopping was a significant part of the life of the household in which Catherine was involved. Helped by the reduction in weight, Catherine stopped using the wheelchair and was able to walk the distances involved quite easily. This gave the impression of a dramatic success early in the life of the house which may well have been important for staff morale. Complete strangers in town stopped staff to tell them how they had noticed Catherine about town for years (after all her appearance was distinctive) and how wonderful it was to see the rapid, recent improvement. Now she could walk! Of course she had already possessed this skill but it was certainly a boost for staff to be credited with this success.

The opportunity to walk, however, also allowed a new problem behaviour to emerge: Catherine would sit, or sometimes lie, down in the street. Again the behaviour was interpreted as being attention-seeking. It was decided that staff should respond by turning slightly away and ignoring her, while keeping a weather-eye open to make sure that she was properly supervised and did not escalate her attempts to gain staff attention to other behaviours which could be damaging. Luckily she never did. When she got up again, staff immediately gave her attention and the walk resumed.

There were some difficulties with this approach. Interpreting the scene as an accident, illness, or injury, passers-by asked whether they could help. Also it was not always possible for Catherine to be out alone with staff and therefore other people from the house had to stand and wait for her. Those who were verbal could not help paying her attention. Moreover, Catherine sometimes chose very unsuitable places to sit down; on one occasion in the middle of the road within sight of police in a nearby patrol car. Independent observation appeared to confirm the hypothesis of attention-seeking. Once while passing in a car, observers saw Catherine and a staff member in the street, with Catherine sitting down. Her eyes were riveted on the staff member and her face showed all the signs of a person waiting in confident expectation that her companion would turn and speak. Although the cause of a behaviour problem may seem clear, action to resolve it can be slow in gaining success. Catherine could sit for very long periods before getting up. If complete consistency in ignoring such behaviour is not achieved in this kind of situation, it is very easy to encourage the person to persevere with the inappropriate behaviour. Waiting for a while and then talking to Catherine might have taught her to carry on sitting down for longer. Staff may have been wanting to complete the trip for the sake of another resident, or because of embarrassment, and so may have inadvertently encouraged the behaviour by paying Catherine attention.

The sight of Catherine sitting down in town had repercussions for the general image of the new venture. A rumour began to develop in Merton which gave a detrimental account. Disquiet was voiced among a group of people connected with one of the local mental handicap voluntary societies. They were mainly parents whose children with mental handicaps, now adult, were still living with them, who might be future users of the service. The parents of people already living in the house, and others directly involved, were not included. A version of events was elaborated to the point that Catherine had been seen in a building contractor's car park (which is passed on the walk between town and the house), lying naked on the ground with a male member of staff on top of her. As far as it was possible to be sure, the event described was one when Catherine did indeed sit down in the car park and stay sitting there for some time. The staff member with her on this occasion was the person-in-charge of the house, who stood waiting for her to get up and even had a conversation with the next-door-neighbour who happened to pass by. The reference to nakedness can only be accounted for by the fact that the rumour was passed throughout a network of people, some of whom knew that Catherine had a history of undressing and remaining naked.

It was perhaps true that in the early days of the house local parents thought that the new venture would not succeed, and that staff would fail to meet the philosophy to which they aspired. Moreover, there was some disagreement over the philosophy in some quarters. This principally concerned the level of demand being made of the people living in the house, the apparent lack of allowance for their handicaps, and the elements of risk which some of the opportunities for involvement in activities entailed; risks which some parents of people with mental handicaps avoided when looking after them at home.

It was important to respond to the rumour before a catalogue of disaster was assembled. The core of the group among whom the bad news was circulating appeared to be a regular social club of older parents who met as part of the activities of their voluntary society. As some of these parents had children who might be served by the house in the future, it was very important not only to correct the factual details of the rumour but to discuss the fears and concerns that might lie behind it. The person-in-charge contacted them and asked whether they would like to hold one of their forthcoming meetings at the house, when they could hear a presentation of the objectives and approaches being taken and have a chance to discuss their own views. That meeting was duly held. The presentation emphasised the positive things about the abilities of the people living in the house which staff were trying to develop and described the kinds of safeguards which had been established. Mrs. Henderson was present and gave her point of view and unconditional support. The meeting went well and, to our knowledge, there have been no more adverse rumours since. Some of the people who attended have begun to ask for short-term care for their children.

Having dealt with that issue well, there remained the immediate problem of how to manage Catherine's walking more effectively. At her first individual programme review meeting, which included all involved professional and service staff and her parents, it became clear that staff of the special care unit used a different method to deal with sitting down on the walks they took from the unit to the local shops. As they usually went in a large group they had no alternative but to lift Catherine straight up again. Not for the only time, the value of having a multi-agency review system, in which all aspects of an individual's life and care programme across the board can be discussed, was brought home to us. As a result the staff of the house reviewed their strategy and decided, especially now that Catherine was lighter and could be lifted more easily, to follow the special care unit procedure. Sitting down was followed by a firm "No", a short command to get up, and a direct lift under the arms. The problem soon disappeared and Catherine subsequently progressed to such an extent that in the summer of the second year she was able to spend a week rambling in Dartmoor.

Developing Catherine's abilities and life style

By the time of Catherine's first individual programme planning meeting six months after moving in, significant progress had been made in reducing the frequency of stripping. Not only were there fewer interruptions to helping Catherine establish alternative behaviours, but staff were less preoccupied with managing the problem. The way was clearer for a concentration on positive development. Even so, the management of Catherine's stripping was still not completed; two more stages were to be passed through.

A change to use of conventional clothing was a high priority following Catherine's weight reduction. This was to occur simultaneously in the three settings which Catherine used: the house, the special care unit, and her parental home which she visited regularly. Catherine, her parents, and staff from the house shopped in preparation for the change, choosing mostly jeans and tee shirts, pullovers, and other similar tops. Everything was blue, the only colour Catherine would wear at the time. Encouraging her to wear other colours and a greater range of clothing, including skirts, dresses, and blouses, was to follow later. The collaboration which had already been established across all three settings was required again to achieve the change. As before, the house staff took the lead. The change to conventional clothing was made during the two-week summer closure of the special care unit. This enabled house staff to ensure that the response to *any* sign of stripping on Catherine's part was consistent under the new conditions of ordinary clothing. It was successful.

Having established the single, effective response already described if Catherine sat down when out walking, one objective set at her first programme review was for Catherine's parents to start taking her out for walks when she stayed with them at week-ends. Once this goal was achieved, Catherine's wheelchair was never used again. She became fully ambulant and was treated as such everywhere she went. The collaboration between house staff, day setting staff, and parents, which is so well-illustrated in relation to Catherine, is a fundamental idea within the system of individual programme review. Catherine's parents are particularly good. Whenever they have had Catherine home, they have been consistent in the way they have treated her, adopting the programme and teaching approaches used in the house. Several factors have contributed to their ability to maintain consistency on the key programme issues of the moment, including: regular contact and discussion; staff demonstrations of management techniques; and having each programme written down. Written programmes include a record of implementation and success as well as programme details. They can be shared by everyone involved and so act as an effective mechanism for maintaining consistency of approach in all settings.

Some major changes to Catherine's life and the way she responded to the people around her began to happen in the first six months or so of living in 10 Summerton Road. The key to her development from that point was in switching from a preoccupation with problem control to the development of pro-social behaviour. The first stages of this lay in teaching her to pay attention to people when they asked for it and then for people to pay attention to her when she was involved in an activity. It was still difficult and hard work for staff to keep up the high level of physical guidance and support needed to keep Catherine reasonably constructively engaged.

A major teaching objective set at the first review meeting was that Catherine should learn to make eye contact on request from staff and to give her attention to staff for a few seconds. Attending on request was formally taught using a graded teaching programme, set and reviewed weekly. Catherine willingly gave her attention to sweets, such as chocolate, and could follow the movement of them with her eyes. Small pieces of chocolate were used, therefore, to encourage her to raise her eyes and look at those of staff doing the teaching in response to the request,

"Catherine, look at me". Each time eye contact was made, a small piece of chocolate was given to Catherine as a reward. Gradually, Catherine had to look more and more towards staff members' eyes on her own, and the interval she maintained gaze was lengthened to a few seconds before she received any chocolate. After a few months of teaching, several times every day, Catherine was able to make eye contact on request unaided, and the use of chocolate as a reward was gradually eliminated. During this time, staff also concentrated on establishing as many natural opportunities as they could throughout the day when Catherine could attend to activities briefly but deliberately; for example, looking in a mirror, or doing simple hand/eye coordination tasks.

Health, appearance and relationship with her family

Parents of people with profound mental handicaps are used to changes being slow. The first year of Catherine's stay at the house was one during which her parents were constantly amazed (and delighted) at the changes made. However, to put her progress into perspective, few of the changes involved developmental growth — a very slow business for someone who is profoundly mentally handicapped. Most of the changes in Catherine's life involved differences in the behaviour of the people around her. This statement is not meant to diminish the work that was done, nor to belittle the significance of change for Catherine. But it does help to reconcile the seeming contradiction in the same person developing tediously slowly for over twenty years and then producing rapid change in a few months. Some people might view such change as in or of the person, and conclude that it might have been wrong to have viewed Catherine as being profoundly mentally handicapped. But she was and still is.

Change occurred because Catherine's diet was modified and, on a healthy, balanced régime, she had lost weight. Staff of the house and the special care unit, as well as Catherine's parents, had agreed a way of responding to her so that she stripped less often and ceased to sit down when out walking. They had bought her new clothes and attended to aspects of her appearance. They worked hard at bridging the gap between Catherine's personal ability and the competencies required to become involved in a full household life. They were directive and supportive rather than permissive: Catherine was not allowed to do exactly as she chose.

Catherine had thin, straight hair that did not grow very well at the back. She began to go to the hairdresser regularly and, with skilled styling and attention, her hair gained body. She drooled badly; the dribble was unsightly on her chin and made a wet area on her clothing underneath. Effort was put into teaching her to allow time to swallow properly at mealtimes, but a review of her medication may also have had a significant impact. Part of the comprehensive review of Catherine's needs addressed the level of tranquillisers she was prescribed and resulted in a reduction of the drug Haloperidol. Following this drooling ceased to be noticeable and this had an immediate beneficial impact on her appearance. Its greater significance, however, may well be for Catherine's long-term health. Such drugs are powerful and not best taken routinely throughout life. With regard to Catherine's excessive facial hair use of a proprietary depilatory cream was effective. Staff then began to investigate how cosmetics would enhance her looks.

Again, it is important to emphasise that, in looking at the action taken in this area, little was to do with changing the ability or skill level of Catherine herself, a woman with a profound mental handicap. It mainly concerned staff activity. Appearance does seem to have an effect upon how a person is regarded by others. If appearance is poor it tends to emphasise the handicap. If appearance is good it promotes the semblance of greater capability. We have shown photographs of the people living at 10 Summerton Road in presentations to staff from other residential settings and have been unable to convince some of them that all of these people are either profoundly or very severely mentally handicapped. The popular association of appearance and extent of handicap is very strong.

Later in Catherine's story behavioural change and change in appearance began to go hand-in-hand. Given a greater head of hair and degree of styling, learning to brush her hair took on greater importance. Her walking improved and she lost some of the ungainliness of her gait. The habit of always wearing flat sandals was changed and her footwear became more fashionable. She was being taught to sit still for longer periods — a matter of seconds at first and then minutes. The impact of her changed appearance and her new-found ability to remain seated in a social group is vividly illustrated in a story told by Catherine's parents. It was a long-standing family custom for the Hendersons to visit close relatives on Christmas morning. After the parents' generation had been chatting for a while, one of the hosts asked, "Where's Catherine?". She had not been recognised as the same person who had visited the previous year. The degree of change had a similar effect on members of the public. A passer-by asked one staff member accompanying Catherine on a trip to town, "Where's the big girl who used to sit down in the street?".

Catherine's relationship with her parents has continued to be a significant part of her life following admission to long-term care. Like Shirley, contact with her parents has been frequent and regular. If anything Catherine has spent even more time in their company; she has gone to stay with them every other week-end, virtually without exception. At first, apart from occasions when her parents came to the house for special social evenings like a New Year party, this was the main form of family contact. Initially both parents, but Catherine's mother in particular, found that short visits to 10 Summerton Road were not helpful because they seemed to upset Catherine. Their arrival seemed to start Catherine stripping with a degree of persistence which would endure even after their departure. However, when staff began to find that the approach within the house was effective in lessening attempts to strip, they began to work with Catherine's parents to help them to carry out the same approach at weekends. Mr. and Mrs. Henderson's contribution and application were superb. They began to get the same results. Although when staff and parents were together Catherine's stripping could still be a problem, her parents began to report complete week-ends during which there had been no instances of stripping at home; something which had taken much effort over many months to establish. Gradually, Mr. and Mrs. Henderson were able to visit 10 Summerton Road without occasioning Catherine to strip. Contact between home and family has subsequently developed freely and without constraint.

Catherine's parents were encouraged to visit her at the house more often, even when there was still difficulty. However, staff and parents realised that, since moving to the house, Catherine was not seeing as frequently the relatives and friends she used to visit with her parents when living at home. Through the individual programme plan system, it was decided to try to keep up the level of these contacts by staff taking Catherine to visit people in her own right. Her parents readily agreed to provide introductions. It was also made clear that friends and relatives could visit

Catherine. If they were in any way shy, they were welcome to come first in the company of Catherine's parents. As a result, Catherine continues to see various friends and relatives independently as well as in the company of her parents.

Catherine's parents and the staff of the house have developed a firm basis of mutual trust and collaboration. They have acted together to formulate and implement a systematic response to Catherine's stripping, to encourage her to walk, to deal with inappropriate episodes of sitting down, to promote self-feeding and improved table manners, to encourage her to remain seated in company, and to arrange their own and other social contacts with Catherine's welfare foremost in mind. Their mutual respect has made it easier to discuss issues of considerable sensitivity, such as whether Catherine should continue to receive injections of long-acting contraceptive medication and whether she should be given contraceptives at all as a routine precaution, and whether in view of her poor teeth she should wear dentures. Both issues were discussed extensively. Contraceptive medication was discontinued. Her parents were not keen at first that she should have false teeth because they thought she might choke on them, so initial dental care centred on restorative work. The feasibility of provision of dentures was subsequently investigated with Catherine's dentist. During the writing of this book, dentures have been fitted and Catherine is learning to use them.

Development and behaviour problems revisited

There is a coherent body of opinion in behavioural psychology that views behaviour problems as an elementary form of non-verbal communication. Catherine had few skills, was deficient in giving attention, found learning extremely difficult, and had only a few words by which to express herself to others. The natural history of the behaviour problems she exhibited seems to fit with a communication hypothesis. The behaviours did not simply disappear; they at first changed in frequency, and then took a different form. They cannot be viewed as permanently replaced. Staff and parents are aware that stripping may return and that they may need to reapply their systematic response to it.

As Catherine's appropriate skills develop and she becomes more able to lead her own life and to communicate with others, she may leave behind such inappropriate behaviour permanently. The fact that such behaviour is likely to return periodically, however, should not be viewed as failure but as a healthy sign. It may show that Catherine's life is not standing still, that new and more difficult things are being demanded and expected of her, and that she is beginning to lead her life without constant adult attention. The important issue is that staff and parents must not be deflected by the absence of a permanent "cure" from returning when necessary to the use of their previously effective approach.

In the first section on Catherine's development, we covered the initial six to nine months in the house: the first stage of the control of stripping, the return to full ambulation, the control of sitting down in the street, the return to conventional clothing, and the teaching of the behaviour of making eye contact and paying attention. These changes provided the basis for continuing development.

The programme to reduce stripping, however, was not complete. Catherine was much improved in this respect but, although remaining undressed for only short periods of time, she still occasionally took off her clothes. Once the blue suits had been discontinued, removal of clothing was restricted to her tee-shirt or other top. A close scrutiny of her behaviour showed that there were two topographical forms to which people had been responding as if they were both part of the same event, namely stripping. (The topography of a behaviour is the description of the precise action, that is, form that the behaviour takes.) One was a right-handed tug upwards from the left side of the neckline of her tee-shirt or other top. The neckline of the garment would be pulled up to about eye-level. Then Catherine would pause and look at staff, and would either stop or continue tugging depending on their response. If staff told her not to do it (that is, gave attention) she would stop. If staff did not respond she would continue. This "tugging" was a high frequency behaviour which acted as a constant irritant and source of interruption. It also damaged Catherine's clothing so that most of her tops became stretched and distorted at the neckline. The other topographical form was a direct removal of her top clothing. To accomplish this, Catherine's right-hand grasped the bottom edge of her top, she lifted her arm straight above her head in one movement, and removed her top in one go.

The recognition of the two different forms of behaviour necessitated a development in the hypothesis concerning the function of Catherine's stripping. Initially attention-seeking had been seen as the reason for the behaviour. A second cause, demand-avoidance, was now added; that is, the ability to stop a task or to avoid a demand. It is likely that Catherine's stripping had always been motivated by both factors. This would help to explain the variability in the length of time Catherine would choose to stay in her room before seeking to re-establish the company of others. The programme was now revised to take account of the likelihood that the two forms of behaviour had different purposes: that the tugging was designed to attract attention, and that full removal of her top was designed to bring current activity to an end and enable Catherine to escape from a situation which made demands on her. The approach to be used by staff to deal with the behaviour was therefore modified as follows:

staff must give Catherine attention at a high rate when she was busy and particularly when she used appropriate forms of communication (words or gesture);

tugging at the neckline of clothing must be greeted by a curt instruction to pull her top down, staff directing both her hands to the bottom of the garment to pull it straight;

staff must be sensitive to activity length and activity difficulty, in an attempt to avoid Catherine wanting to escape from situations;

staff must continue to exclude Catherine from the communal life of the house for a brief period following removal of clothing, dressing her again at the end of the period and then re-engaging her in activity.

As the new approach was adopted the place to which Catherine was excluded was changed from her bedroom to the bathroom. Now that Catherine was becoming involved in hair styling, grooming, and the use of make-up, she found her bedroom a pleasant place to be. It was therefore thought to be an ineffective place to which to continue to exclude her, particularly as a time-out strategy was no longer regarded as the most obvious management approach. If the hypothesis that Catherine was signalling a wish to stop an activity was correct, going into "time-out" was one way for her to achieve the desired outcome. In these circumstances, stripping might be expected to persist. Added to this, staff did not want Catherine to regard her bedroom as a place of punishment.

This change in strategy soon made an impact in a fairly dramatic way. Catherine spent a turbulent week-end in the house when she damaged property and pulled staff members' hair. She tipped over and broke her own record player and she pulled curtains down from the rail. All these behaviours were familiar to her parents, Catherine having displayed them in the past. It seemed that in the frustration of finding her dominant problem behaviour being blocked from achieving its accustomed ends, Catherine was bringing in others from her past experience. The person-in-charge of the house was called in for advice. Staff responded calmly, knowing that a wrong response by them to the new behaviours could easily establish them as an ongoing problem. By Monday evening, the tantrum had subsided and the new behaviours fell back into abeyance. Catherine no longer tugged at the neckline of her clothes.

Periodic bursts of stripping still occur occasionally at the house. As we have said, this may be a healthy sign — that staff require more of Catherine as she develops; but they may sometimes make the mistake of demanding too much from her, either in terms of length of attention or complexity of activity. In response Catherine may show signs of stripping and, because of the length of time since they last used the set procedure, staff may naturally respond by trying to prevent her from doing so. Finding that the old consequences of her behaviour are back again Catherine quickly increases its frequency. The set programme is then reinstated. Having experienced this natural cycle of events staff have learned from it. They now know the perils of doing anything other than following the laid down procedure. Their learning has been reinforced by the fact that when they have followed the procedure they have avoided an increase in Catherine's attempts to strip.

Stripping has also continued in the settings in which Catherine spends the day, seemingly as a result of inconsistency in management. The problem is greatest in the special care unit where some days are dominated by Catherine stripping repeatedly, a fact that illustrates the specificity of the relationship between individuals' behaviour and their immediate environment. Just because Catherine has learned not to do a behaviour (that is, the behaviour is ineffective) in her own house and that of her parents does not guarantee she will not do it in a third setting if staff there do not manage it appropriately. Given that management within the special care unit has not been entirely successful there have been short-term carry-over effects when Catherine has returned home. However, these have lessened with time.

Having succeeded in greatly reducing Catherine's prevailing form of stripping (the physical removal of clothing), staff and parents were next presented with a verbal variant: the request "change". Catherine asked repeatedly to change her clothing. This she did at any time throughout the day but, possibly due to the carry-over effect already mentioned, she asked most frequently following return from the special care unit. Initially staff and parents indulged the request, finding it distinctly preferable to actual stripping. After some months however, this behaviour too became tedious and wasted a considerable amount of everyone's time. A concerted attempt by staff and parents to refuse the request met with success.

Work on developing more positive aspects of Catherine's life continued. The initial teaching of attention, together with the constant daily practice of participating in the household routine, was beginning to result in a greater willingness on Catherine's part to stay in one place and become involved. The length of time she would sit down in a social situation gradually increased. She became able to go to a pub or café and behave appropriately and to sit patiently at the hairdresser's. There has been a remarkable achievement in respect of dental work. Whereas before all dental work had to be done under general anaesthetic, more recently a local anaesthetic has been sufficient, with Catherine voluntarily sitting long enough to allow the treatment to be undertaken.

While basic attentional control was being taught, simple self-care skills were also being targeted. Catherine was taught to eat using a fork and spoon together and, following this, to chew her food more slowly and to swallow well. She had always eaten with her chin well forward, over and almost in her food, so she has been taught to sit up straight and to raise the food to her mouth. Towards the end of her second year in the house, she had progressed to eating with a knife and fork. At about this time, teaching of dressing was begun (she could undress well already!). She was also taught to wash herself and to sit longer for an activity.

About the house and in town Catherine is able to do most things with the support of staff. She participates in all types of food preparation, clearing away, domestic, and laundry tasks in the house; she joins in the gardening; and she goes shopping and visits pubs and cafés, the hairdresser's, and the theatre. She has begun swimming, not in a special class or association for the disabled, but as an ordinary member of the public. The skills she required in all these activities were identified and taught, such as: the ability to sit in a pub after finishing her own drink while others finished theirs; how to clear the table after a meal; and how to take rinsed dishes from the sink and place them on the drainer.

Throughout this time, but particularly after the initial management of difficult behaviour was accomplished, it has been important to encourage Catherine in her use of language, both in the breadth of her vocabulary and in the sophistication of her expressive speech. She has changed from having a few single slurred words to having a considerably expanded vocabulary, a clearer and more adult articulation, and the ability to use words in pairs and phrases. Her most sophisticated utterances now are simple phrase and sentence constructions of up to about four words. A recent teaching goal is for her to learn to sit, look at a picture, and have a conversation about it with someone for three minutes.

Catherine's dressing has improved and she can now put on her own pants, tops, jeans, and shoes. She still needs help with her bra and with tights. Even so, on the occasions, rare now, when she strips she has the dressing skills necessary to regulate for herself how long she need stay away from the mainstream life of the house.

Current life

In this account we have tried to convey an impression of considerable change, which has had a dramatic impact on one person's life style and which has the potential for even greater possibilities. Catherine's way of life has shifted from that of an overgrown, difficult child who lived at home and went to bed early, to that of a young adult who keeps adult hours and shares a daily routine with others that is similar to that followed by the general community. But not by any stretch of the imagination has Catherine been made normal; she will always be regarded as having a profound or very severe mental handicap. Currently a programme is under way to try to establish night-time continence and her coordination is so poor that she is working on a target designed to enable her to drink from a cup without spilling. She follows an exercise programme to tone up her muscle structure, partly to tighten up her skin which was stretched by being so much overweight but also because, like many other people with profound handicaps, her limbs have been relatively underused in the past. But perhaps in the fitness boom of the eighties having such a programme is not unusual!

Catherine lives independently of her parents, in a staff supported house in the town in which she has grown up. She is likely to continue to live there for many years to come, if not the rest of her life, should it suit her and should she require it. Monday to Friday she attends the special care unit of the local adult training centre, as she did before moving to the house. The curriculum there resembles one for nursery or infant children, and during the past three years, Catherine's programme has changed little *in character* although it may have changed in detail. That does not mean that there have been no successes in teaching her specific skills or that changes in routine have not occurred. For example, Catherine has made progress in naming pictures and she no longer eats her lunch in the special care unit itself, instead taking lunch in the main dining hall. But the contrast between her working life and her home life illustrates the interaction that can occur given certain characteristics in the setting and the personal characteristics of an individual.

Catherine is the same person in both settings. The changes in the character of her life at home have come about in a setting designed to offer the same opportunities that people who are not handicapped enjoy in similar settings. It is the job of the staff to exploit these opportunities ingeniously and deliberately, to the maximum benefit of the individual who is handicapped. A hard look at the special care unit, on the other hand, reveals a setting which possesses few of the opportunities usually available in work places for staff to exploit. The staff are as handicapped by the environment of the unit and the orientation it generates as the service users.

On week-days, Catherine returns to the house around 4.00 pm. She may attend first to personal concerns but then there will be chores to be done. These vary from helping to prepare the evening meal, cleaning her bedroom, doing the washing, or going shopping. Usually the evening meal is taken between 6.00 and 6.30 pm. Sometimes, the people who go shopping at the end of the afternoon eat out and do not return until later. After the meal, the washing up must be done and everything must be put away. People usually have a cup of coffee together, either directly after the meal or a little later. Some evenings Catherine goes out: to the pub, or to the house of a friend or relative, or to some recreational event. Sometimes she has visitors. Sometimes she just stays at home, perhaps doing some housework, or enjoying the chance of a longer bath than usual, or involved in a one-off activity with the others, or following an interest of her own. For example, she has begun to use a camera and is assembling a photograph album. She usually goes to bed some time between 9.30 and 11.30 pm, possibly later on special occasions.

Catherine goes to stay with her parents on alternate week-ends. These occasions are pleasant for all concerned. Her parents involve her in more activities these days. She helps her father in the garden. Sometimes they go out and watch a game of cricket. She shows pleasure anticipating a week-end with her parents. Afterwards she is also clearly happy to return to her own home. Her parents visit her on the week-ends she is not staying with them and they often call in mid-week too. Catherine sometimes "drops in" on her mother for coffee.

Each year the people living at 10 Summerton Road go on holiday. They go in pairs, together with two members of staff, to a place of their choosing. In the first summer, Catherine was still seen as someone who presented major management problems. The holiday chosen for her was a number of successive day excursions, returning to the house every evening. In the second summer, Catherine went for a walking holiday in Dartmoor. The next year she went to stay in a rented cottage on the coast. The accompanying staff were surprised by the independence she displayed on this last holiday; advances over and above those that had developed at home. She was content to sit in the cottage for long periods and she was particularly communicative, speaking in short sentences. She started helpful activities on her own. For example, she set the table, asking for help to find the things to be laid. She tidied up unprompted, picking up any clothes on her bedroom floor and trying to put them away. When she had finished with her coffee cup, she took it to the kitchen and put it in the sink. At dusk she drew the curtains in both rooms of the cottage and switched on the light without being asked. In fact she was generally helpful with household tasks and needed less physical guidance than usual. Staff also noted how well she had accomplished some self-care skills. For example, she ate more competently, using a knife and fork. She needed few reminders on how to stab food with the fork and she remembered to put her knife and fork down between mouthfuls giving herself time to chew well and eat slowly. She did not wear an apron (as she usually does in the house) and made little mess.

Mr. and Mrs. Henderson's view

Catherine's parents have this to say about the impact that the changes of the last three years have had on their lives:

Mr. H.: *"The difference it has made in our lives since Catherine has been away is that it has taken all the tension out of it. We used to be on duty twenty-four hours a day. Now we can relax, and it's the first time we've really relaxed for 22 years. We are living a totally different life and enjoying life; relaxing, which at our age we need to."*

Mrs. H.: *"We were just about at the end of our tether, I believe. I felt that life was like a spring wound up which was going ping all the time and I was really worried. It was at least an eighteen hour day. I don't watch the clock now as I did then. I knew other people watched the clock and had time settings for everything. I did. I didn't have very much time for myself really — you could say from 10.00 in the morning til 3.00 in the afternoon — and there had to be a lot of work done in that amount of time. I had to do all my work, shopping, go to the hairdresser's, and get all the housework done at home. Catherine would be up anything from 5.00 am onwards and it was a case of working towards going to the Special Care Unit at 10.00. Very often, we would be ready earlier. We would have long bathing sessions but still be ready to go to the Centre far too early. I would take her out and drive her around in the car until it was time to get there. The other people going to Special Care, the ones that did get there early, were the ones who came on the organised transport. I took Catherine every day and fetched her. I think I was supposed to collect her at 3.00 but I did not go until 3.30 to pick her up — well, between 3.00 and 3.30 anyway."*

Mr. H.: *"We used to spend hours and hours, travelling miles and miles, driving around just to keep Catherine happy. It was far better than being in the house where she appeared to be unhappy — well, not so much unhappy but naughty — driving round and round, it* *was a way to pass the time. Really we passed our life away just to keep the peace with Catherine."*

Mrs. H.: *"Yes, that's quite true. We tried several things, but we weren't very happy about her going away. The happiest time was when she went to the Junior Training Centre in (town) during the week and came home at weekends. That seemed to work very well but, of course, when she became sixteen and an adult she had to change over to the Training Centre here."*

Mr. H.: *"We always said that that had a lot of effect on Catherine, didn't it?"*

Mrs. H.: *"Yes, change."*

Mr. H.: *"It was strange. She was happy to go away for the week and come home weekends and was happy to go back again. When she had to leave . . . she became extremely naughty."*

Mrs. H.: *"Very difficult."*

Mr. H.: *"Very difficult, yes. Because she missed the school. She didn't like the change. That is Catherine's biggest problem, it's change. I think they find this with new members of staff: new faces. A new person comes and she tries to play them up and get the better of them — until she's beaten them — and in the end it's anything for a quiet life".*

Mrs. H.: *"It's quite true."*

Mr. H.: *"At the Special Care Unit, they followed the same approach as us — is there anything to keep Catherine quiet? When they started up at 10 Summerton Road, they started with a completely new method and stuck with it. That is what has proved to be the right thing, in Catherine's case."*

Mrs. H.: *"We've tried to follow that method as well but I don't think they have always been able to do that at Special Care."*

Mr. H.: *"We would never have thought of letting Catherine do things herself because we would do everything for her. We kept her away from touching anything. The method at 10 Summerton Road, to make her do things and make her be as independent as possible, has worked. If you could see Catherine when she went into 10 Summerton Road and now; they have worked absolute miracles. She is a thousand per cent better because she has been made to feel* *like someone, I think, feel like a human being in her mind. She is someone now, before she was nothing. I'm sure, in her own mind she feels that way. She is living in the community now. She goes out shopping, where we pushed her around in a wheelchair. She wouldn't walk more than half-a-dozen steps without sitting down so we had to get the wheelchair just to be mobile. We can now arrange things we could never have done before. We can now go places we could never have gone before. Prior to Catherine moving into Summerton Road, if ever we were invited out or asked to join in something we said, 'We will have to wait to see if we can get a babysitter'. We could only ever get one person to babysit because she was the only person Catherine would accept. They seemed to hit it off and get on with one another, and Catherine was very fond of her. So we always had to get in touch with her first: 'Can you come on a certain night? Yes? Then we can make arrangements'. We daren't make any arrangements beforehand with the fear that the babysitter wasn't available. So in that way our lives were completely tied down. Now we are free to say, 'Yes, we will go down there' or 'We will do this', and plan ahead. We couldn't plan more than a day ahead before, could we?"*

Mrs. H.: *"No. I worked nights and people used to invite me to do things during the day. I could only agree to things between 10.00 and 3.00 but I always used to say, 'Yes, God willing'. People had to understand that I might not be able to, for if Catherine was ill then that was it, I couldn't go. Even though she was that age, I was still curtailed as if I had a toddler.*

I haven't yet said about how easy it was going to be having Catherine in Summerton Road. She would be on my doorstep. But I didn't realise how much I would miss her, and that I would still be watching the clock and I would be thinking, 'Yes, she will be coming out of Special Care just now' and wondering what sort of day she had had. In the morning, I would think, 'She is just going now', and I was still watching the clock even though she wasn't here."

Mr. H.: *"In the evening, we would sit and talk, wondering what she would be doing, wondering whether she was behaving herself. I think it was out of relief as much as missing her. We could sit back, relieved in our own minds, and be able to talk; hoping she would make it, because we always had our doubts that her behaviour problem would be too great and we would see her back on the* *doorstep again."*

Mrs. H.: *"Yes, I did worry about it."*

Mr. H.: *"We worried whether she would make it."*

Mrs. H.: *"We haven't had a very easy time with other people looking after Catherine. It's always a strain and we've always had the feeling that it's been very difficult for them. When we've got back when we have been away it was clear it's always been very difficult for them."* (Do you mean for services?) *"Yes. They never told you when you were away, but when you got back. We always realised that Catherine had been quite difficult."*

Mr. H.: *"She went into two hostels while we went on holiday and each time she caused havoc. When we 'phoned up while we were away they had said, 'Don't worry, she's OK'. When we got back they hadn't coped with her and we would suffer terribly for two or three weeks after that, while Catherine would appear to take it out on us for leaving her there. And then, in the later stages, we went for three or four years without a holiday. Then we were talked into letting her go into . . . Hospital. She went in there on two occasions and she came out in such a state on both of these occasions that we vowed we would never let her go again. We always said that we didn't blame the staff because there were only two staff to 30 residents and, no matter how hard they worked, they couldn't cope."*

Mrs. H.: *"She went into . . . Hospital for a weekend once a month because when we knew Summerton Road was going to open we thought we would try to get her used to going away. Do you remember that?"*

Mr. H.: *"Yes. We had a programme of stays. The consultant psychiatrist asked for that to give us a break because we were really getting to the end of our tether. Terrible, the trouble is remembering what we felt. It's very difficult to remember. We feel very rested now and we were very, very tired then. It's a funny thing, people ask how we coped, but it became an everyday pattern of life for us. We never thought about not coping. It was part of our lives and we really forgot what life was all about, normal life. Other people enjoying life could not understand it. We were so tied down and said, 'We can't do this', 'We can't do that'. They'd say, 'Why can't you do it?'. They didn't realise. We just took it for everyday life. We didn't* *complain about it."*

Mrs. H.: *"I always said that whatever you have got to do, you can do. Whatever life presents you, if you are determined, you can do it."*

Mr. H.: *"It was our burden and we carried it. It became natural life for us in the end. We can honestly say that when Catherine went into Summerton Road we were lost. We were walking around, no noise, no havoc, no tension — we were lost."*

Mrs. H.: *"The tension was quite severe, like being on a spring all the time. For instance, when cooking I was always scared of her being burned. Something happens and you think, 'What shall I do — turn it off, take it with me?'. Catherine would never come with me if there was something on the cooker. If the telephone rang when I was cooking, it could cause havoc."*

Mr. H.: *"And in the latter stages when she was stripping so much, if anyone knocked the door — well, there was all hell let loose while we tried to get her into her room. One of us would sit in the room with her while the other opened the door."*

Mrs. H.: *"I was on my own and the door used to go."*

Mr. H.: *"Yes, or in the evening, when Mrs. H. worked, there was me keeping them standing on the doorstep and trying to push Catherine back saying, 'Would you hold on a moment?', explaining in the end that I had a handicapped daughter and I didn't think she was fully dressed at the time and could they just hold on. And if they had to come in, to try and whip them into the lounge and try to get Catherine to see a little bit of cooperation; and if not put her in her room. You had to put her in her room and leave her there while you spoke to the person. It was terribly difficult dealing with strangers."*

Mrs. H.: *"I found that, of the tradespeople coming in, the insurance man was the most difficult. You would have to go into details . . ."*

Mr. H.: *"Catherine would burst out with nothing on."*

Mrs. H.: *"I'd have a cheque written out. I got very skilled at getting things done very much in advance. I'd get the cheque all written out, you know, and put ready."*

Mr. H.: *"If someone came to the door we had to put Catherine into another room, close a couple of doors to give us a chance to sort the* *person out before Catherine got out and got to the front door. The tension was that great."*

Mrs. H.: *"So it's very difficult now to assess how we felt."*

Mr. H.: *"It seems an age ago. It's three years ago and it seems an age — as though we never really had it. It's just something that you have to rake your mind about to know what really did happen. It's very difficult to picture now. Looking back on it, I don't think we could have carried on much longer. Summerton Road opened up just at the right time to save us, I think. One of us would have gone I am sure of it, because at times we felt terribly ill. The lack of sleep was one of the worst things. I had meetings at work, having been up since 4.00 in the morning, and I found myself dozing off and it became a worry. For your job you know. You felt you were slipping behind because you couldn't get to grips with it — you were so worn out. Although we used to share as much as we could . . ."*

Mrs. H.: *"I used to do everything during the week really and you used to cover weekends. And you used to say I could catch up on my sleep then but I really couldn't. I used to fall asleep sometimes. If I dared to sit down in the afternoon, I'd be away. Mrs. R.* (senior instructor at the Special Care Unit), *to give her credit, used to say if I didn't get there on time they would say I'd fallen asleep and they would leave me and then would ring about 4.00. It was like having a heart attack when the phone rang. I would tear up there and fetch her. I would fly in and make all my apologies and they would say, 'We knew you were asleep, you must be asleep'. Perhaps about once a month I would do that. I used to find that I could hardly crawl out to go to work at 6.00 o'clock. About an hour later people used to say 'You look better now'. It was when I would begin to relax. I went to work to relax."*

Mr. H.: *"The doctor actually said that it was a good thing for her. It was fortunate that she could go to work in the evening and that I could come home and take over."*

Mrs. H.: *"That was the only reason I could do it. I would not have had a job if I hadn't found out that they took night staff. So I applied to go back. I couldn't do a day job because I knew I couldn't keep it up if Catherine was ill or in school holidays — you couldn't keep a job going. That was the thing that kept me sane, going to work kept me sane. If I couldn't have I would have been in a mental illness* *hospital myself, if I couldn't have gone out and had some privacy."*

Mr. H.: *"And then it got to a stage that we could never take Catherine anywhere, to anybody else's house, without her being terribly naughty unless she got her own way. So we just stopped taking her out. Now we take her down to Paul and Anne's* (brother and sister-in-law) *and the grandchildren, and she is good as gold there. And recently we took her down to my sister-in-law in Somerset and we had lunch down there and came back in the afternoon and they were amazed, weren't they? They never thought they would see Catherine acting the way she did. Paul said he never ever thought he would see Catherine using a knife and fork. She will sit at the table now with a knife and fork, whereas before it used to be head down bolting away at her food. It's absolutely remarkable the progress she has made. Everybody, our friends all state it, what a remarkable change. She's a different child — oh yes, I mustn't say child — sorry, I always say that.*

To us, Catherine was always a baby, wasn't she? A baby. We used the term babysitter when we shouldn't have done. We still did that when she was 20, she was always a baby. Now, Catherine appears to us more as an adult. She's far more intelligent, she must have had intelligence there before but she shows more intelligence. She is so well behaved now. It's difficult to say, we've loved Catherine always; but there were times we got to the end of our tether with her — oh God, feeling anything but love at times — but we never ever smacked her, we never scolded her. Well, we might have scolded her but we never smacked her, did we?"

Mrs. H.: *"No."*

Mr. H.: *"We refrained from that, but I think the affection, that's the word I think, is growing now with her because she is so good. She comes home at weekends now and she is so good that you are proud of her. Yes. Whereas before you could not feel proud of her. You can feel proud because she has made so much progress and she's so much warmer to us, isn't she? When she comes home now, weekends, we'll sit in on a Saturday night, the three of us, on the settee, and watch the television. It's been up to two hours, Catherine sitting with her head laying on you and actually watching the television. Three years ago she wouldn't sit down for two seconds. She just wouldn't sit down in fact. And now, she'll sit down for long spells; and she'll sit at the table after she's had her meal and wait for* *the others to finish."*

Mrs. H.: *"We are enjoying our time with Catherine more."*

Mr. H.: *"We look forward to her weekends, coming home."*

Mrs. H.: *"We don't really relax much when she's at home do we, even now?"*

Mr. H.: *"When she's home we devote the whole weekend to Catherine. We made up our minds that every other weekend we would make no arrangements unless it was to take Catherine visiting, or something like that. The whole weekend is devoted and centred around Catherine and, for all the rest of the time, we are absolutely free agents. We've never known that in our lives before."*

(Are there any other sorts of things that you do now? Things you spend a lot of time on where you couldn't or didn't before?)

Mr. H.: *"Sit down."*

Mrs. H.: *"Enjoy our own home, I think it is one of the greatest pleasures, do you not think so? Strangely enough, although we say we can go out, we don't now, not so much as we did."*

Mr. H.: *"We used to go far more when Catherine was at home than ever we do now. Since Catherine has been at Summerton Road, I don't think we go out a third as much as we used to — it was getting out, getting someone in to look after Catherine and just getting out we wanted; but now we don't want to. We've got the house and the garden and we are happy to spend our time at home in peace and quiet and I think that's one of the main things — peace and quiet."*

Mrs. H.: *"We do live quite busy lives, although I complain that I'm not doing as much as I did. I haven't got the strength. But it's still quite a busy life really. You know, the girls at work tell me I do too much."*

Mr. H.: *"I go to quite a lot of meetings you know, but hopefully I shall start curbing those."*

Mrs. H.: *"I don't know what I'm going to do when I retire next year if he's out as much as he is. There comes a limit to the amount of charity work you can do."*

Mr. H.: *"I have to go to a lot of meetings for the firm."*

Mrs. H.: *"I know you do."*

Mr. H.: *"Well, I would say that Summerton Road has put ten years on our lives and I mean that sincerely. I thank Summerton Road for saving our lives and I say that with all sincerity. When we heard that Summerton Road was opening and that it was for people with profound handicaps, we almost did a highland fling — when we thought there was a possible chance for Catherine. As we said earlier, we did not think she would survive — with her behaviour. We don't mean any disrespect but, at the time, we were scared that they wouldn't be able to handle her."*

Mrs. H.: *"Well, we'd had so many bad experiences."*

Mr. H.: *"Nobody ever handled Catherine."*

Mrs. H.: *"And we weren't making a very good job of it."*

Mr. H.: *"No, we made a hash of it in the end. It's our fault in the end. We had to give up trying to keep Catherine dressed, otherwise we wouldn't have done a thing. We couldn't have decorated, we couldn't have done anything in the house unless we had let Catherine strip. When she'd done it Catherine would be happy and would sit down or walk up and down and we could get on with any work. It came to the point, when we were trying and trying to keep her dressed and trying to keep good behaviour, when we were doing absolutely nothing."*

Mrs. H.: *"And it's not just one day. It was day in, day out; week in, week out."*

Mr. H.: *"Everything was getting neglected, trying to look after Catherine."*

Mrs. H.: *"You know the outlook has changed such a lot. When Catherine was a baby we were told at Great Ormond Street never to expect very much, not to expect anything. You were not given any guidelines. It's bad enough I think for ordinary parents. Parents have a great responsibility with an ordinary child. I have always thought that parents don't realise what they are letting themselves in for. It's a great responsibility, and everyone has to have trials and errors; but, with a handicapped child, it's even worse and you were not really given . . . well, perhaps you are now . . . given advice. And you didn't really think about it — you always thought that what she was doing was because of her condition. You didn't relate it to the fact that she was just like an ordinary human being who didn't* *have the ability to learn quite as well. So, you always felt it was to do with her disability; it was her brain telling her to do something, when really she should have been treated just normally. This sitting down business — if you had a toddler doing that, you would leave him sitting in the street and walk away. You'd say, 'I'm off, and if you are not coming . . .'. When you get somebody aged twenty doing that, then it becomes very difficult."*

Mr. H.: *"She was so terribly heavy that you couldn't pick her up. It was impossible to move her because she had some built in way of preventing you from lifting her. She would lie there in such a way that you just couldn't move her; she was a dead weight."*

Mrs. H.: *"Well, I certainly could not go back to doing that again, so I hope that houses like Summerton Road will survive. Well, I wouldn't have to because she's changed, hasn't she?"*

Mr. H.: *"Well, I'm sure that they will survive and the only thing that I hope is that Catherine stays at Summerton Road for the rest of her life. One thing Catherine does not like is change — I think we are all agreed on that. She changes her attitude when there is any change, so I hope to goodness that she stays at Summerton Road and I'm sure she will always be very happy there.*

One of our biggest worries was that, before Summerton Road opened, we knew that if anything happened to us Catherine was destined for a mental hospital. With her behaviour problems, she would have gone into rather unpleasant surroundings. That was one of our biggest fears; to try and face up to the fact that that was where Catherine would end up. Because it was obvious. We always said to Paul, 'You may feel as though you want to have her but you must never burden yourself with her; but always make sure she is well looked after'. You see, that is another thing that Summerton Road has taken care of — it's taken the burden off our minds. What's going to happen to her when we are gone? Now we know that she is going to be safe and happy.

We said earlier that we used to go every Christmas to friends for a drink on Christmas morning. If Catherine was not happy, we used to be there for about three minutes and one of us would have to come back. This was before she went to Summerton Road. It was last year our friends didn't even know Catherine was there. They said that they didn't realise that it was Catherine. It was absolutely true. She sat down for an hour or an hour-and-a-half."

Mrs. H.: *"I don't know, I didn't stay there drinking too long because I see three turkeys if I do . . ."*

Mr. H.: *"They said, 'That's not Catherine because she's slim and good and she's sat there on the settee with Paul and Anne'. It just wasn't her, for usually she took over; she was the centre of attention wherever she went.*

Mrs. H.: *"That is one of the things that is beginning to get ironed out isn't it. Last Friday night* (party at Summerton Road) *she didn't want to be the centre of attention."*

Mr. H.: *"Yes, she was lost amongst the crowd on Friday night. She's growing up isn't she? I know, we are absolutely thrilled."*

Mrs. H.: *"One of the things I wanted to say is that I'm delighted in the staff at Summerton Road. I was always very pleased to see a mixture of staff ages, and young members of staff of Catherine's age."*

Mr. H.: *"This has been one of the greatest assets."*

Mrs. H.: *"As well as the older members of staff who can give the mothering. I think that it is a very good thing and I have always been delighted about it. You have the young ones with all the enthusiasm and the knowledge of what they like doing at Catherine's age, and then you get the older ones who say, 'Well, perhaps we want an extra pullover today as it's a bit cold'."*

Mr. H.: *"There's another thing that did please me very much which I would like to mention. I know Catherine's hairdresser quite well. When she first went there he said he chased her round and round, from one chair to another, and did a clip at a time. After about two hours he finally got a bit of hair off. And the last time she went there, he said to me, 'I was amazed that Catherine sat in the chair, never moved, and let me set and restyle her hair completely'. The hairdresser said that he had never seen such a change in a person. The day she came in here with her hair permed we could have jumped for joy, couldn't we? She looked lovely. We never thought it was possible. So, all these little things that keep coming to mind are the things that have given us so much pleasure, the things that we thought could never possibly happen; and they are happening. They keep coming to mind — all these little things such as hair . . . make-up. She comes home with eye shadow and rouge, and she looks like a filmstar sometimes."*

Mrs. H.: *"And they are all so expert at putting it on, I'm not so expert at doing it."*

Mr. H.: *"And the most important thing is her clothes. She started off with that old suit that she used to wear, strapped up at the back; but still she used to fight her way out of it. Now she comes home in the most beautiful clothes and looks very smart."*

Mrs. H.: *"I was very pleased with the last pair of jeans, with the belt — I've never been able to get a belt on Catherine."*

Mr. H.: *"She looks lovely in some of the jumpers and blouses she wears. But before, she never looked lovely. You could almost say she was ugly — fat; and that blue suit, it made her look awful, didn't it?*

Mrs. H.: *"She has lovely eyes."*

CHAPTER 4

Mary M . . . — family contact is not the only consideration

The wisdom of moving people with mental handicaps who are in, or are approaching, old age and who have been accustomed to institutional life for many decades is one issue that those developing alternative services are certain to encounter. Although barely middle-aged, the fact that Shirley had spent thirty-five years in a large hospital led her father and sisters to be uncertain which choice to make in her best interests. The same issue arose with respect to Mary, a woman aged fifty-three, who had been in residential care for over forty years.

A second issue is that of moving people from an institutional setting to a local service some distance away. Most people can see the sense of this if family members live nearby who are keen to continue or resume active contact. But what if they have lost, or have deliberately withdrawn, contact for many years? Should someone who is mentally handicapped be left in an adverse situation simply because of lack of interest on the part of the family? In Mary's case this second issue was also present, and in a form for which we were less than well-prepared; namely, an extreme conflict between her mother's opposition to the suggested move and what we saw as being in Mary's best interests.

The relevance of these two issues in terms of Mary's experience of moving to an ordinary house in the community is sharpened by the fact that, eighteen months after her transfer, she died. Compared with the four decades she had spent in two institutions, eighteen months is a short time; but, as our account should show, the effort in striving for improved care for people who may only experience it for a relatively short time is not wasted.

When 10 Summerton Road was being planned, Mary was resident in one of England's three special security hospitals for mentally abnormal offenders. She had not been found guilty of a crime by the courts but had been transferred there because of disruptive and aggressive behaviour in the mental handicap hospital where she had lived previously. She was detained under the sixth schedule of the *Mental Health Act, 1959,* by an order which was renewed every two years until 1980. Mary was eligible for a place in the house because her mother, now elderly and widowed, lived in its catchment area and because the house sought to serve all adults with severe or profound mental handicaps whose lack of functional ability merited the intensity of staffing provided. After initial contact was made, it was clear to us that Mary had been effectively abandoned by her family.

In describing the situation in such objective terms we do not wish to engender a lack of sympathy towards Mary's family. Her mother, Mrs. M., often acting on advice, had done what she thought was best, not only for herself and other members of her family, but also for Mary. It was a situation to which she had become adjusted, though it had caused her emotional difficulty throughout her life. The unexpected contact from staff of the local service was another source of disturbance. Our approach came as a considerable shock and it was immediately obvious on visiting her home to discuss the opportunity for Mary to transfer to 10 Summerton Road that the proposal caused her serious distress. She had experienced difficulty in sleeping since she had received the letter from the consultant psychiatrist requesting the visit. She had seen her general practitioner for medication because of her state of anxiety, and she spoke openly of a possible breakdown if the matter were to continue or if Mary were to be moved to the locality. She maintained the view that, if the purpose of our visit was to obtain her permission to such a move, she categorically refused to give it.

On discussing the issue with Mrs. M. we were both sympathetic to her and concerned for her state of health. We did not want the tranquility of her life in old age to be overturned. On the other hand, we recognised our responsibility as representatives of Mary's welfare. We also recognised a wider responsibility; that of encouraging local services to accept individuals who were no longer appropriately placed in the special hospitals. We felt that the plight of the special hospitals and their residents would remain unaltered if local service authorities showed no resolve in finding alternative placements for those who were fit to leave.

We soon realised that Mrs. M. had few people to turn to for personal support in this unforeseen difficulty. Only one member of her immediate family even knew of Mary's existence, and she was unwilling for him to be approached or involved in the discussions. She also refused to disclose the name of her doctor in order that the psychiatrist could professionally consult her medical advisor. The conflict of interest between the welfare of the mother and that of the daughter seemed irreconcilable; even to the extent that continuing the discussion could be viewed as an unjustifiable intrusion likely to be seriously detrimental to the mother's mental state.

From the little information gained from our one meeting, it seemed that the crux of the problem involved two factors. One was the social embarrassment that would arise for the family, and the mother in particular, should it become known that there was a family member with a mental handicap whose existence had been denied. The other was the prediction that, if Mary moved to the locality, it would not be possible to keep her identity concealed. Mary's family was well-to-do. Her mother was sure that her distinctive surname would soon be associated with her family if it became known locally. She was concerned about the reaction of the rest of the family, her friends and neighbours, and the local press if the situation came to light. She could not see why her grandchildren should be forced to come to terms with the discovery that they had an aunt who was "peculiar and severely handicapped".

Mary had been admitted to a mental handicap hospital near London as a child. During the Second World War, there was a period in which Mrs. M. did not see her, which resulted in a deterioration in their relationship. Mrs. M. had then been advised by her own general practitioner and the staff of the mental handicap hospital to make a complete break, in the best interests of both Mary and herself. The hospital staff asked her not to visit, as Mary became disturbed afterwards. Subsequently, Mrs. M. had been kept informed by the relevant authority of Mary's place of care and any serious episodes in her life, such as the illness that had brought her close to dying. She sent money for staff to buy Mary Christmas presents. She had adjusted to not seeing Mary any more and did not wish to face further change so late in life.

Understandably, Mrs. M. viewed Mary as a woman who was severely mentally handicapped and behaviourally difficult, who had developed little in her fifty years, and had posed such extreme problems of management that it had been necessary to transfer her from one mental handicap hospital to another, and then finally to a state security hospital. She had become totally dependent on service authorities for knowledge of her daughter; and this was the impression that they conveyed.

Although Mrs. M. appreciated the sincerity and good intentions behind our representations, and although she was aware of concerns over the quality of care provided in the state security hospital in which Mary was living in particular, and in large institutions in general, it must have seemed to her insane to suggest that Mary could move to live in an ordinary residential road in the middle of her local town and be managed successfully. She saw her daughter being the centre of a public disturbance, followed by inevitable press coverage.

Of the limited information Mrs. M. had received about Mary in her rare dealings with the services, much was to do with difficulties. She knew, for example, that Mary banged her head against the wall in temper, and that she attacked others. If Mary moved Mrs. M. would have to make a terrible decision: whether to re-establish contact with her or not. She was probably sure in her own mind that she would not. This would be difficult though for, if she continued to shop in the local town, she would have to pass 10 Summerton Road knowing it was where her daughter lived; in a repeated act of ignoring her existence rather than the current, more passive denial. She also wondered whether she would recognise Mary should there be a chance meeting in town.

We were faced with many questions. Who was the client of the service? What rights did parents of adults with mental handicaps and the adults themselves have respectively? Who should represent the welfare of an adult who, because of mental handicap and language deficiency, could not make a reasonable, informed choice? How should a decision to take a course of action in support of one individual's welfare be weighed if there was a possibility that it would be seriously damaging to another's? Mary's mother talked not only of nervous breakdown but also of taking an overdose to end her life. But the moral dilemma was transitive: failure to take a course of action to benefit one indiviudal, in order to protect the interests of another, presented an equally unsatisfactory conclusion.

In our deliberations, the following factors seemed relevant. Firstly, the initial opinion that Mary would be likely to benefit from the transfer remained unchanged. The route out of the difficulty should not be found by adjusting our assessment of the extent of benefit Mary might be predicted to gain from the transfer. Establishing greater family contact through providing local services is only one of a number of possible benefits. Even with no contact from her family, the increased opportunities available to Mary within the type of care planned were seen as having considerable potential to benefit other aspects of her life. Therefore, if she were not transferred simply as a result of parental opposition, the service could be guilty of implicitly judging her welfare as being of secondary importance.

Secondly, there needed to be some judgement of the likely consequences for both parties. This was the central issue. Although difficult it had to be faced. There was no doubt about the level of Mrs. M.'s distress; but there was at least a possibility that this might be alleviated by the passage of time and with the aid of those who were close to her. If Mary was not transferred to her local service authority, it was fairly certain that she would remain in hospital for the rest of her life. Exactly how damaging that would be to her was unknown. Certainly she would never be aware herself of a missed opportunity for improvement but such a consideration did not materially change the fact that, in not acting on her behalf, we would be condemning her to spend the rest of her days with a quality of life lower than it might otherwise have been.

Thirdly, it appeared relevant to consider the normal parent/adult child relationship. In considering this issue most of us had experienced acting, as adults, in opposition to our parents' wishes and, therefore, we took the view that parents are not necessarily unbiased representatives of their children's welfare. We could not simply concede our responsibility to Mary by considering her mother's view paramount. We agreed, as a matter of principle, that the parents of an adult with a mental handicap had the right to be informed of matters concerning that adult but not the right to give or withhold permission in that regard.

Lastly, there were some bureaucratic policy considerations. We felt that our local service should support the reduction in size of the special hospitals but could envisage many forms of opposition to the placing of people from special hospitals in the community. We felt, however, that if local services did not act with some determination to accept former residents of the special hospitals the size of those institutions would remain unchanged. We also felt that, within the National Health Service generally, there was an active principle that although people had a right to treatment, the professionals involved retained some discretion on the place and nature of the service.

These last considerations may be considered as the insensitive hand of bureaucracy. But returning to Mary's mother's position, the fatalism which she expressed of the bureaucracy doing as it had intended irrespective of her wishes was the only sign that she had at least countenanced the possibility that Mary would indeed move to Summerton Road. The person-in-charge of the new house visited Mrs. M. again, alone this time, after he had been to see Mary and the circumstances of her care in the special hospital. He had two aims: to describe the philosophy of the proposed service, the opportunities it offered Mary, and the safeguards that would be built into the model by the high level of staffing and day-to-day structure; and, secondly, to discuss ways in which the service might act to overcome her fear of disclosure of identity and subsequent public notoriety. Any option was worth considering, even that of Mary adopting a different surname. The person-in-charge gave a guarantee of complete confidentiality on the part of the service. He also guaranteed that no further contact with the family would ever be made by the service. In fact, if she chose, Mrs. M. need never know whether Mary had moved or not.

After his second visit, Mary's mother wrote to the person-in-charge. This letter influenced the views of the members of the case conference which considered and recommended Mary's transfer, one phrase being seen as giving tacit agreement to the transfer subject to the two guarantees. Staff at Summerton Road were never informed of Mary's family background and were instructed never to use her surname in conversation with any outside party. This was in line with the general requirement not to talk about the concerns of any person living at the house except to other service staff. The guarantee of no contact was kept until it was necessary to inform the family that Mary was seriously ill with an inoperable brain tumour.

A second letter from Mary's mother enclosed a Christmas present. She was thanked and informed that it had been put to good use. The complete absence of further contact meant we were unable to discover just how much distress Mrs. M. suffered as a result of Mary's transfer, so a complete assessment of the wisdom of the decision can never be reached.

Mary: before moving

Mary moved to 10 Summerton Road in the second week of November, from an environment which had aspects of prison security, such as being confined to a locked dormitory from early evening until morning. Her contact with the outside world was non-existent and her behaviour, the cause of her transfer to the special hospital, was disruptive. She displayed temper tantrums at least two or three times a week. These were sometimes so intense that she fell to the floor and forcibly removed her clothing. She also damaged property, pummelling surfaces with her fists and breaking windows. She had attacked staff over a long period but these outbursts, as well as the more extreme forms of self-injury she had once shown, had declined. Her disruptiveness, therefore, should perhaps not be overstated. She was living on a pre-discharge ward and her move was considered appropriate by the professionals involved in her care.

Mary had a severe mental handicap and few self-help skills. She ate using a spoon and her fingers, could drink unassisted but with considerable spilling, and could dress (given that she wore loose tops and elasticated trousers) with help. She was fully ambulant but with a lop-sided gait. She was generally continent but did not wash even her hands herself. On the *Fairview Self-help Scale* in 1976 she obtained a score of 31.4 months. Reassessed in 1978, she scored only 19.9 months. Whether she had regressed or whether scales of this kind are prone to such variability is open to debate. The ward staff gave no indication of anything other than Mary being in a fairly stable state. After the move, she was assessed again, scoring a mental age of 28 months.

Mary was extremely sociable, to the point of inappropriateness. She would greet even total strangers in an intimate way, putting her arms round them in a bearhug and kissing them. She would physically hold on to people and not let go. Such actions were accompanied by very limited and repetitive speech. She was physically affectionate to people sitting next to her and would grasp their forearms or rub their backs and say, "I like you, I like you . . .". Her entire vocabulary comprised a few phrases and a number of odd words which she used in delayed, echolalic fashion. She could identify a few objects but could not distinguish between the sexes or follow simple instructions. Her personal possessions were gathered constantly around her in bags and on her person. She was said to hoard rubbish up her sleeves and to become frustrated when thwarted, showing temper by stamping her feet, slamming doors, and throwing herself to the floor screaming. She also collected and hoarded books and had no appreciation of other people's property. She was described as being jealous of attention shown to others. Although very sociable when it suited her she could sometimes be withdrawn, often choosing to sit or lie on the floor, inactive, away from others. She was seen as stubborn and persistent in her idleness; attempts to direct her into an activity group were frequently met with temper tantrums.

Mary's appearance on arrival at the house was not flattering to her. She had thick black hair which had only a rudimentary style and lacked lustre. Her face showed signs of damage (she was reported as rubbing and picking it, causing sores and injury). She had a few disordered teeth and no dentures. She had little clothing: some underwear, a few round-necked pullovers and trousers with elasticated tops, an anorak, and a pair of shoes which, although new, were about two sizes too big. Her personal belongings were two large and worn teddy bears and some well-thumbed fashion catalogues. She took them with her wherever she went and thumbed through the catalogues repetitively.

Strategies for change: what can be done immediately?

As in other accounts told here, the kind of health care, quality of clothing, and attention to personal appearance which people with very severe or profound mental handicaps receive is dependent on other people's activity on their behalf. Their resulting health and appearance should not be seen as a function of the extent of their handicap but rather of the care or neglect of the service. These areas have the potential for immediate change. Progress does not require greater personal competence on the part of the person who is handicapped, something which is a genuinely slow business to achieve. It does require that the objective to improve aspects of the person's health and appearance be specified and that staff seek for and safeguard quality in these respects. It also requires that staff numbers are sufficient to allow time to be spent achieving and maintaining progress. Numbers and time in themselves, however, are not enough. It is also necessary to set standards for achievement, and these need to be taken from the non-handicapped world.

The importance of presentable appearance is manifest in the attention it receives in today's world; in advertising and in the amount of money spent on fashion, clothing, and hairstyling. In thinking about whether these are important to people with severe mental handicaps a number of considerations are relevant. Firstly there is self-image: will the person appreciate his or her own appearance? We think so on the whole but we do not always know. We are sure, however, that it is important to assume that someone with even the most severe mental handicap can be aware of interpersonal differences and can take pride in looking good. This is an assumption which protects quality; adopting the opposite viewpoint can only lead to the possibility of neglect. Secondly, personal appearance affects the perception others have of a person. Poor appearance seems to be unpleasant to other people and generates avoidance. If someone has a behavioural handicap which also produces this response it is important to avoid compounding the problem. As we have mentioned before, audiences find it difficult to believe that the people we illustrate in talks about 10 Summerton Road really have severe and profound mental handicaps. They associate good appearance with greater ability and better functioning. Thirdly, in a service which sets community integration as one of its goals, good appearance is part of a reasonable bargain with the community-at-large. Social integration involves acceptance; and this can be helped or hindered by appearance as well as by behavioural characteristics. An emphasis on presentable appearance lessens the extent to which it is necessary to appeal for a special attitude to be shown by the community to its members with mental handicaps.

In the first six months after moving to Summerton Road, Mary received an extra share of the clothing budget in order to purchase a suitable range to her wardrobe — a new top coat, dresses, and shoes. As well as looking right, it was found that more fashionable, adult ladies' shoes with a slight heel helped her to walk with a more normal gait. She went to the hairdresser and the chiropodist, and began a course of dental treatment leading to the provision of dentures. She was proud of her new appearance. She liked having her hair done and enjoyed brushing it herself. Apart from a slight awkwardness in movement, in time Mary's appearance gave little indication of her handicap.

It is important to emphasise that in distinguishing the issues of ability and appearance, and in highlighting the separate importance of appearance, the presence of a real, functional handicap is not being denied. It is true that an individual's behavioural deficiencies or problems can make the task of attending to appearance more difficult. For example, when Mary received her dentures she had difficulty in wearing them without gagging. This might have been due to the dentures not fitting properly, which in turn could have been due to the difficulty of obtaining an adequate impression. Mary was not able to help the dentist as other people might. There was also the question of teaching her to wear them; getting her used to having teeth after many years of being without any. Thus in order to attend to this aspect of her appearance, staff had to embark on a long-term programme of structuring increasingly longer occasions when Mary would wear her dentures. If they were successful in achieving even short but significant usage, the dentist was willing to put further effort into obtaining a more precise moulding that would fit Mary more closely.

This example illustrates the complexity of coordination and effort that may be required to obtain personal characteristics for individuals with handicaps which accord with the broad range of standards for other people. There is an interaction between seeking high quality involvement from the various branches of the helping professions and developing individuals' behaviour appropriate to the activities involved in maintaining such standards, achieving personal care, or using materials to good effect. However, in relation to people with severe and profound mental handicaps, learning can neither be achieved quickly nor on a broad front simultaneously. It is, therefore, necessary to be wise in making decisions as to what to teach. The targets chosen need to be important to the life of the individual.

It is also necessary to consider when to teach. A teaching strategy for wearing dentures was unavoidable, given that nobody could help Mary by wearing her dentures for her. However, an alternative strategy to teaching is often possible in which staff help to bridge the gap between personal accomplishment of the individual and what is required. In many ways staff can act as a prosthetic device. Just as spectacles bridge the gap between the current ability of an individual's eyes and the visual acuity needed, staff act as a social prosthesis helping the person who is handicapped to behave as others do in similar environmental circumstances. The analogy with spectacles also helps to give an image of the extent of help to be given. In just the same way as an overly strong prescription for glasses will lead to a deterioration in the muscles of the eye and an increasing dependence and worsening of sight, excessive staff help leads to overdependence and often overprotection. Staff must give the minimal help required and allow the person to contribute personally as much as possible. As in the other stories in this book, direct involvement in household life following this strategy of staff support had a direct and major impact on Mary's life style. Into this fitted the more selective construction of teaching programmes.

Behavioural development

Early priorities for teaching were concerned with improving Mary's mode of eating, her table manners, and her ability to wash and to dress, and gaining her cooperation in joining in the activities of the house and getting more appropriate social interaction. The temper tantrums and screaming described in hospital Mary probably displayed in order to avoid demands, to avoid becoming involved, and to keep herself to herself. For example, it was found that she particularly disliked washing her hands, and the cracks in the plaster above the handbasin in the kitchen at Summerton Road still bear testimony to her displeasure at being requested to do so for herself. Mary generally needed coaxing to carry out any domestic assignments. If already sitting down she would often say "No, no, no" to any request to do something. Therefore, in order to preserve the normal social convention of asking her whether she would like to do something, rather than telling her, while at the same time keeping to the objective to promote Mary's meaningful occupation, staff learned to ask her to get up and come with them, suggesting the intended activity to her a few seconds after she had stood up.

As Mary became used to joining in more and learning simple domestic tasks, such as emptying the dishwasher or pegging out the washing, her agreement to follow requests became easier to obtain. Once occupied, she participated with good grace, enjoying the social situation. However, care had to be taken not to let one task be merged into a second or third; a common strategy which attempts to translate agreement to one request into another rather than facing the situation of seeking agreement to a new request. Mary liked to celebrate her achievement by saying, "I done it", and then returning to the living room to sit down. Care had to be taken to allow her the opportunity to be pleased at having done what she had been asked to do before asking something else of her. The breaks between activities did not have to be prolonged.

In this way, there were relatively few occasions on which there was major conflict between Mary's will and that of staff. The destructive behaviours and serious temper tantrums displayed in hospital were encountered relatively infrequently. Early on, she broke a few windows and there was a more protracted problem concerning handwashing. This was the subject of a specific structured programme, organised on similar lines to the more general approach which staff were beginning to learn was the most appropriate mode of interaction. Mary used to scream and hit the wall above the washbasin. Staff responded to her outbursts consistently by saying "No" sternly and turning away from her. Once the tantrum had stopped, they repeated the request while at the same time guiding her to be successful.

There is some research literature that has looked at systematically varying the level of difficulty of demands made of people with mental handicaps who display inappropriate behaviour in order to avoid situations. Demands for simple tasks which an individual is capable of doing may be met with compliance while requests for more complicated activities, which may still appear exceedingly simple to staff, may generate disturbed behaviour. Experience with Mary seemed to fit well with such an analysis. She was extremely sociable, enjoyed praise, and articulated accomplishment. At the same time she had been considered in her previous environments to be stubborn and difficult to occupy in activities, other than those she chose for herself which were almost always lacking in adaptive function. As she became more competent, however, she became more ready to participate though staff had to remain sensitive to her real understanding of language and avoid increasing the difficulty of their demands beyond her level of development.

During the year following her transfer, Mary had a thorough, progressive review of her medication. On arrival, she was being prescribed 200mg Epilim twice a day, 5mg Valium morning and night, and 10ml chloral hydrate at night. She was also written up for 100mg Largactil by intra-muscular injection when needed. The chloral hydrate and Largactil were immediately stopped. With a longer waking day and progress toward a new sleeping pattern it was predicted, correctly, that Mary would sleep without need of medication. And it was not intended that any behavioural disturbance would be treated by sedation. The Valium was reduced shortly afterwards. Meanwhile the psychiatrist wrote to the special hospital to find out whether the Epilim had been prescribed as a result of a history of epilepsy or as a response to

Mary's behavioural disturbance. The reply indicated that epilepsy had never been apparent, so the Epilim too was gradually reduced once the administration of Valium had been phased out entirely. By the end of 1982, Mary was receiving no medication at all and the psychiatrist's notes record improving behaviour alongside drug reduction.

Her physical ability was also reviewed. Although having the use of all four limbs Mary was found to be restricted in movement on one side. The local physiotherapist was consulted, who was able to design about ten arm and hand exercises to strengthen her weak side. Mary worked on these with the aid of the staff of the house.

The new opportunities that were available to Mary within the general context of staff support led to fairly rapid development. She quickly learned to use a knife and fork at mealtimes. She was so thrilled with this new accomplishment at first that for a few weeks she chose to eat everything by that means, even her toast and marmalade at breakfast. In hospital she had been described as taking food from others' plates and being terribly messy, but now she learned to wait for others to finish before taking more, to offer serving dishes (when prompted) to others, and to use language to express preferences and wants. Her proficiency at eating unaided improved enormously.

She also participated in the routine domestic tasks of the house: clearing the dining table and putting the things on the kitchen hatch, wiping surfaces, sweeping or vacuuming the floors, cleaning her own room and helping with the communal ones, dusting ornaments, doing the washing, hanging clothes out, taking them in, ironing, putting clothes in the airing cupboard, and removing them from there to the wardrobe and drawers in her room. She went shopping almost daily. It is true that the majority of these things were done with staff instruction and direct guidance, but through regular practice and some specific teaching Mary increased considerably the part she played and the level of independence she displayed. For example, she became gradually more competent at aligning and positioning different types of crockery and cutlery in the dishwasher so that in time she could load it herself when asked. She could also empty it and put the crockery and cutlery away in cupboards and drawers.

Specifically programmed teaching taught Mary many whole and component skills for her personal care and household life. She was taught to wash her hands using soap; and then to dry them. Once she had learnt this the tantrums that she had thrown when asked to wash her hands died out. Having learned this successfully she was taught to wash her face using soap and flannel, and to dry her face, neck, arms, front, and groin after bathing. She learned to look in a mirror while brushing her hair, first for three seconds, then for five, and then for seven seconds. She became able to unscrew and remove the cap from the toothpaste tube and to clean her teeth on both sides. She learned to put clothes on a hanger and hang them in her wardrobe, to put folded items neatly in drawers, and to look for and take out required items without totally disturbing the remaining contents. Mary was accustomed to undressing by pulling off all garments worn above the waist together, and all those worn below the waist together. This damaged her clothing and also meant that it needed to be unravelled before she could redress. So Mary was taught to take items off singly. By careful structuring of natural opportunities Mary learned to collect the dirty washing from people's rooms and bring it to the laundry room, and to wash small items of clothing by hand. She placed objects in cupboards or on surfaces on request, that is, she developed an understanding of the prepositions "in" and "on". She learned to drink without spilling, to put a half-full milk jug in the fridge without spilling, to fetch, empty, and return the office wastepaper bin, to take full bags from the kitchen bin and put them in the outdoor dustbin, to hold a dustpan for someone else to sweep into, to sweep garden leaves into a pile, to vacuum the carpet, to tip liquid left in cups down the sink before upturning them in the dishwasher, to wash up (alongside another person), to dry saucepans, to fill teacups to the correct level from jug or teapot (first with and then without a verbal instruction), and to take a pillow case off a pillow.

Other changes important to Mary's development occurred in relation to her language and socialisation, both in the house and outside. Mary had an extremely sociable personality which should have been reviewed as an asset but her pattern of social interaction was so odd that her sociability had been cast as an inappropriate trait. Her repetitive speech was extremely wearing and the way she approached and greeted people could be off-putting, particularly to the unaware. She physically grasped and held on to people and was generally over-intimate. As someone who had moved back to the locality from placement far afield, there was no immediate prospect of Mary receiving any day-care service. Her life style was one of a middle-aged housewife who could shop daily for bread, meat, and fresh vegetables if she so chose. Having previously lived under prison security, Mary's experience of this side of life had been greatly restricted. Going to shops and having a meal in a restaurant or a drink in a pub represented significant new opportunities for her. If she were to gain the best possible benefit from her new environment and avoid the kind of negative reaction which her mother had predicted, it was an urgent matter for Mary to be taught more appropriate social skills.

At first, Mary greeted all visitors to the house, people returning to the house, and even people inside the house in an inappropriate manner. In order to teach her to keep an appropriate distance and to offer her hand to shake instead, every physical contact Mary initiated in an overly-intimate way was met by an impassive correction. This comprised releasing her grasp, moving back slightly, taking her right hand to an offering position, taking her hand and shaking it, and at that point smiling and saying the normal social pleasantries. This was rapidly successful in shaping her interactions with people within or coming to the house. A similar effort was made when Mary reached for and held people while shopping, such as a cashier or sales assistant. She was physically corrected and verbally reprimanded. Mary had a particular tendency to address staff in supermarket overalls as "nurse"; understandable, given the limitations of her experience over many years. This too was discouraged. Her improved appearance, now smart and presentable, may well have counted for little if her mode of interaction had not changed. Gradually, however, she learned to offer her hand in greeting rather than to embrace people, and to distinguish between people she knew and those who were strangers.

Another factor that was detrimental to Mary's image and her ability to participate effectively in the domestic round was a habit of carrying her possessions around with her, particularly two large and worn teddy bears. Although these were never taken outside the house, early on they went everywhere with her inside. In the same way that Shirley's doll's pram had considerable potential for projecting a continuing juvenile impression, irrespective of other changes which might be made, so too had the battered teddies. However, unlike Shirley's pram the phenomenon did not correct itself by virtue of the other opportunities in the house. A positive approach had to be followed in an attempt to supplant their role in

Mary's life by acquiring other, more age-appropriate accessories which she would prefer to keep with her. Mary was encouraged to purchase a handbag. Given the interest shown in it by the people round her and the opportunity it gave her to be similar to adult women in her immediate surroundings, Mary began to choose to take this with her instead of the teddies. The handbag also served as a repository for other items Mary treasured — a number of handkerchiefs, combs, and some small picture books. In time, she was taught to put her handbag down when in the house and to collect it when going out or moving to sit in another room. Moreover, as her personal property increased, her tendency to hoard items reduced. The teddies, at first kept in her bedroom, were eventually discarded.

Community living, recreational pursuits, and social life

Mary had many chances to go shopping and to visit cafés and pubs for refreshment. She was able to push the trolley in a supermarket and to collect goods from shelves with instruction. She learned to wait for change when making purchases, and to buy herself a Coke in a café. Her sociability led to many genuine social exchanges as she became a familiar and regular customer in the locality. She had a tendency to show people she did not know very well what she had bought, such as when she purchased some new earrings. This still marked her out as being socially immature for her age; but it was a far more preferable and appealing peculiarity than her earlier means of contacting people.

One story can illustrate how well Mary was accepted within the community. She had become a regular shopper at a local bakery. One day, when the shop was particularly crowded, Mary and a member of staff entered the baker's and waited at the back of the queue. Totally on the assistant's initiation, Mary was asked to help serve behind the counter. The assistant said something like, "Come on Mary, come and help — we are busy . . . This lady wants six bread rolls in this bag here". Between the shop assistant and Mary, the lady was served. When Mary later became terminally ill, many people asked after her. Although she knew no-one when she came to the locality, some thirty people attended her funeral (the combined staff and resident group at that time was only seventeen).

Within the house, Mary contributed fully to the household routine. More than any of the others she also organised her own leisure activities. She liked to look at books and to do simple interlocking jigsaws, an accomplishment she brought with her from hospital. She continued these activities, choosing to get out jigsaws or books from the cupboard when not otherwise busy in the house. When she needed something to work on she collected one of a nest of tables and placed it by an armchair in the living room. Although the activities themselves were not new, there was some development in the way Mary pursued them. When she first moved to the house Mary gave every impression of being someone who had lived in an environment in which personal belongings were not respected: in hospital she had gathered all her possessions to her person in a number of carrier bags and kept them with her wherever she went. When first in the house she had carried the teddy bears with her. When they were replaced with the handbag she carried that with her just as much to begin with, using it to collect and keep small possessions. As time went by Mary was taught to reduce the number of items she carried around with her and to keep her belongings in the cupboards available in the living room and her own bedroom. She gradually learned that, in this house, other people would not interfere with her personal belongings. The small, childish books she had brought with her were replaced by more adult books, these retaining a similar emphasis on pictures; for example, books on nature, gardening, and travel. These were too large to fit into a lady's handbag and had to be kept on the shelves in the living room. Her puzzles and other recreational materials were kept in the cupboard above the books. Therefore, although Mary continued the kind of recreational pursuits she had followed in hospital, her new home environment provided a different and more preferable context for such activities. Leisure became an activity of choice, fitted in between personal and domestic chores, which Mary organised for herself. She learned to undertake the more extended sequence of arranging her environment: getting a table out, getting the materials from the cupboard, and putting everything away afterwards. She could at last rely on the fact that it was possible to have personal belongings within a group setting which would be safe if she left them unattended.

Mary was also interested in watching television and she liked listening to music. She learned how to turn the television on and off to gain greater independence in this respect. She shared these interests with Carol (see next chapter) who had a stereo and a television set in her own room. Mary was often invited by Carol to watch television with her in Carol's room — a special form of companionship. Mary began to arrange and keep a photograph album which she liked to look through periodically. With modern cameras, photography is a simple hobby that can be enjoyed by people with severe mental handicaps. Unfortunately, its expense is a considerable barrier and serves to illustrate the personal poverty of most people with such handicaps in our society.

In the time after moving to Summerton Road Mary went to the cinema a number of times, went to music concerts, attended church, visited a riding stables and attended a gymkhana, went on all-day shopping excursions to neighbouring cities, ate lunch and dinner out in restaurants, visited the homes of staff, used public transport, and played pub skittles. Many of these events occurred in the evening. Mary kept the hours of an adult; a distinct difference to her life in hospital. Holidays were another new form of activity. In the one summer that followed her move to the house, Mary had spent a holiday with Shirley and two members of staff in a caravan at a seaside resort. The caravan park had a restaurant, bar, and entertainment complex which they used as adults.

At the onset of Mary's illness, further avenues for recreation were being explored. These would have involved her in more extended community contact. One possibility was horse-riding, which would have been started through Riding for the Disabled and subsequently continued independently. Another was regular attendance at lunchtime concerts at the local college of further education.

Mary had no family contact as explained earlier. She did build up a personal friendship with a few local citizens, something that staff tried to encourage due to her particular circumstances. Apart from the relatives of other people living in the house four people visited Mary. Two developed a particular friendship with her. The shop assistant who had invited Mary to serve bread rolls in the baker's shop became a regular visitor. Her fiancé (later her husband) also became involved. They visited Mary at the house and also did other things which friends generally do, such as when meeting her in town unexpectedly, deciding to go off together to a café for a coffee. Mary was able to entertain them at home, offering them coffee (with staff help) or inviting them to stay for a meal. Staff fostered the friendship and began to talk to the couple about whether they would be prepared to act as external advocates for Mary's welfare at her six-monthly individual programme planning review meetings. They had agreed to do so and would have attended the next meeting in that capacity if Mary's illness had not intervened. Mary was invited to and attended their wedding.

Mary appeared to be extremely happy in her new life. Staff took a consistent approach to her tantrums and the behaviours that were damaging to property. Their decline, however, may equally well be attributable to the generally more stimulating environment, Mary's own increasing capability, and the direct experience of the results of her contribution to household life. A structured approach to changing Mary's initial tendency towards non-compliance into a likelihood of cooperation was important in maximising her development and the use of the opportunities available to her. Care always had to be exercised in inviting Mary to engage in household activity; without it she could easily refuse.

In a world of greater activity, greater material enrichment including personal possessions and a range of clothing, more opportunity to go shopping for food, household requirements, and personal belongings (toiletries, cosmetics, tissues, and jewellery), and increased social contact, Mary's vocabulary increased by leaps and bounds. This development was aided by her echolalic capacity to copy speech. Learning what objects were called was not difficult for her; she had a well-established tendency to imitate other people. In order for her speech to develop some functional meaning, all that was required was the consistent creation of situations in which she needed to use language in order to obtain the outcome she wanted. Her sociability gave her a strong desire to gain other people's interest in and approval for what she was doing. It is very likely that her developing language helped her sustain her sociable world.

Mary's use of language however always remained repetitive in character and on a bad day could still be wearing. It was typical for her to show someone a personal possession, such as a new pair of slippers, saying "slippers", "new", "pretty". This would be repeated, not only several times in a single episode but from one day to the next, until they could hardly be regarded as new. Her considerably expanded vocabulary did have the benefit of diluting the particular nature of her repetitive speech and allowing a much greater pool of possible utterances and subjects to be discussed.

More to the point, although Mary's language retained its repetitious character, not all of her expression was echolalic. She was able to answer questions and state preferences or choices without repeating herself.

Serious illness

It was around the time of Mary's second Christmas in the house that staff first began to observe worrying signs. She appeared a little frail at times — showing a slight stumble, a lack of balance, or a failure to stand up from the armchair at first attempt. She also started to become slightly less cooperative again. She had always had a minor physical disability causing weakness on one side and staff were well aware of her tendency to refuse requests, so neither problem was new. Her increased non-compliance was also a matter of only a slight change in degree. It was nothing like the level of refusal to join in which had characterised her early days in the house. Even so, staff were sensitive to these changes and raised them for discussion at the weekly staff meeting. Two courses of action were agreed. One was for staff to be especially careful about the difficulty of the requests they made of Mary and the length of participation they expected of her. In other words, the procedures which had worked in establishing her greater participation in the first place were reinstated. The other was to consult Mary's general practitioner and psychiatrist for medical examination and opinion. Early in the onset of her illness, later diagnosed as a brain tumour, medical examination did not detect any untoward clinical signs and the psychiatric advice did not add to the management strategy already adopted. Therefore, no specific action arose from this line of inquiry.

Over the next two months, the signs which had first alerted staff that something was wrong accelerated and Mary started to hit her head and pull out her hair. Even if staff could contemplate Mary going to such lengths to be left alone (which they found difficult to accept), the form of disruptive behaviour chosen struck them as incongruous. In the past, her opposition had taken a different form — temper tantrums involving screaming and hitting floor, table, or wall with her fists — so why had she not returned to these rather than adopting a different behaviour? Mary had also become particularly proud of her appearance, especially of her hair. Staff therefore suspected that she was experiencing pain and again asked for a medical opinion. This led eventually to a full neurological examination, but not before Mary had pulled out most of her hair. The effect on staff, on Mary's friends, and on everyone else who knew her was extremely upsetting. None of them was able to accelerate the processes which might gain Mary respite from her suffering, which had now become all too evident. Staff had shown sensitivity in their identification and interpretation of the early behavioural signs of growing distress. They then experienced delay in gaining appropriate examination and medical referral.

Mary was admitted to the neurological unit of the nearest teaching hospital. There, a rapidly-growing and inoperable brain tumour was diagnosed. Mary was given medication to relieve the pressure within her head which, in expert opinion, must have caused her considerable pain. She remained an inpatient for about a week, the medication successfully controlling pain as judged by the cessation of hair-pulling. As there was no curative treatment possible she was deemed ready to return home.

The fact that Mary returned to her home at 10 Summerton Road, and was cared for there during the last stages of her terminal illness, is relevant to the current debate over the ability of ordinary community settings to cater for specialist problems. Arguments in favour of community care should not be interpreted as being incompatible with special arrangements being made for people when necessary. There is a considerable emphasis within the principle of normalisation on catering for individual need by the most powerful and intense strategies available. A competent service would be expected to make specialist (different) arrangements specific to each individual's requirements. But in doing so, it should also seek to keep unaltered all other arrangements that are important to an individual which are not in need of change. Thus, when Mary's conspicuous need was for neurological examination she received it, as other citizens would, in the normal specialist way which involved a temporary stay away from home. However, once the need for accurate assessment, diagnosis, and decision-making concerning treatment had been met, new requirements became paramount.

The service responded by allowing her to pass her last days in comfort, in familiar surroundings, and among the people she knew best. Mary, therefore, returned to Summerton Road where arrangements had been made to ensure her comfort and care. She moved to a bedroom on the ground floor, where a hospital bed was installed to make lifting and turning easier (the easier it was for staff, the more comfortable it would be for Mary), and discussions were held with the community nursing service so that they could be called upon if necessary. The two senior staff at the house were trained nurses but they were not specialists in caring for a dying person. However, their experience helped them to teach the other staff how to give Mary food and drink, how to care for her skin, and how to lift her into and out of a bath. The community nursing service gave specialist advice but did not supply direct labour. It had been envisaged that they might make domiciliary visits to help with bathing and toileting and with turning at night. However, when Mary became so frail that house staff were concerned that she would suffer undue discomfort from being handled by just one person, they devised a rota of sleeping-over duties so that day-staff could provide the additional pair of hands required. This initiative was supported by senior management who provided appropriate additional payment.

With these arrangements for her comfort and nursing care, Mary was still able to have what benefits she could appreciate from home life. Other people living in the house, on returning from their day-care settings, often went to Mary's room to see how she was. At least two showed visible concern. Afternoon tea was taken together in Mary's room and she was visited frequently by friends. Her care was beyond reproach, a credit to the staff. She died in June 1983.

A final consideration

Mary had lived for forty years in specialist institutions providing residential care for people with mental handicaps. She had spent a quarter of a century in her last place of residence, a state security hospital. No doubt she was accustomed to the life. The decision that she should be moved to 10 Summerton Road was complicated by more than the usual number of doubts which often attend such new ventures. These mainly concerned her family. But in addition Mary was detained under a Section of the *Mental Health Act, 1959* and this required that official DHSS sanction had to be given to her transfer. (The Section was eventually lifted, not to be renewed, some seven months before her death.) Although it is not unusual for people to move from security hospitals while their Sections are still in force, and such official restrictions are not automatically proof of extreme difficulty in personal behaviour, it is much less common for them to move directly to a small community setting.

Had Mary been older, say in her late sixties rather than her early fifties, the proposition that she was accustomed to institutional life, that it was "too late", and that it would therefore be personally detrimental to move her might have been made with some force. It is never quite clear whether the area of concern in such arguments is based on the individual's limited life expectancy and the view that such temporary disruption to the individual is not justified, or on the assumption that, at a certain age, making any form of change becomes too difficult. From our experience of a number of people with mental handicaps who have moved to new homes on various occasions, we think that the extent of the disruption can be overstated. This may be particularly true for people with more severe handicaps who, because of their relative lack of skills, may have established few strong interpersonal ties. Mary, unexpectedly, only lived under changed circumstances for a short time, a little over eighteen months. Clearly some balance needs to be drawn; but no-one who was involved with her after the move doubted the wisdom of it or the benefit she experienced from her new life up to the onset of illness.

Traditionally, provision of residential care for people with mental handicaps, inherited from our predecessors, has been in the form of large institutions. We do not wish in any way to question the concern of the staff in these institutions for the welfare and the care of their charges. Nonetheless, there has been a growing movement towards a policy of building appropriate services to care for people within the community. The onus of proof is still on the care in the community developments to demonstrate that individuals do benefit from a life in a community setting as opposed to one in the traditional form of provision. Those familiar with the means by which the benefits of a service arrangement are often judged in relation to people with mental handicaps, will recognise the emphasis given to developmental progress and the growth of skills. Such developments essentially reverse the defining condition; the absence of capability and the slowness in learning which is called mental handicap.

This account of Mary has described behavioural development, how she grew in independence. But at the end, that growth in skill comes to nought, reversed first by illness and then by death. What is left as having perhaps been more significant to Mary in her life is the actual character of life in the house, something which is more difficult to describe and needs more detail to capture: the routine round of her daily experience, the opportunities for participation and contribution, the increased breadth of experience, and the purposeful nature of the involvement she had with her material and social world. It seems to matter very little that before she became ill she had become marginally more skilled than before. The importance of that development was in how it contributed to the way she led her life from day to day. She was still an impossible distance away from ever becoming an independent adult. The benefit of the change is that she lived in an environment which supported the best use of the capabilities she possessed and enabled her to maximise her own contribution, allowing her access to some of the good things of life. Without claiming that the quality of service in the house was perfect, it is possible to claim that through its philosophy there were aspects of life style and opportunity afforded to Mary which most people would consider preferable to those available to her in her previous circumstances. The measure of benefit is that she experienced these for 592 days.

CHAPTER 5

Carol Brown — developing independence in familiar surroundings

Carol Brown had lived in Merton for most of her life. Well into middle-age she lived at home, at first with both parents and then, after the death of her father, with her mother alone. However, immediately before moving to 10 Summerton Road, Carol had been living in a residential facility in a town some thirty miles away, towards the other end of the same health district. She had gone there when her mother had become senile and was in need of care herself. Admission to residential care is frequently the only service response when the supporting arrangements for a person with a mental handicap living in the community break down. This, coupled with a lack of suitable services locally, meant that the best that could be offered Carol was a transfer away from her familiar surroundings to a new life in a strange setting.

This kind of enforced move, away from home and familiar locality, cannot be an unusual occurrence. It must be true for most people admitted to large residential institutions. Carol might well be considered to have fared rather better than most. She did not go to the mental handicap hospital which officially served her town, which was some seven or eight miles further away, but to a relatively new, small, purpose-built, community-based hostel. It had been provided in the mid-1970's, the time when the care in the community policy was beginning to be introduced. It was intended to serve the town in which it was located. Carol's admission contravened its catchment area policy, but was sanctioned as an emergency, short-term measure. When her mother died, however, Carol became a permanent resident and ended up staying there for three years.

Three years is not a short time, but for Carol, a person with a mental handicap living in residential care, the chance to return to her home town so soon must be considered unusual and a matter of good fortune. Development of local residential services for people with mental handicaps has been slow; many people never have the opportunity to move from their existing residential placements. There is also a view that new local services should be used primarily for people in need who are already living in the locality rather than for bringing back people who have had to move away. This proposition tends to grow in strength the longer an individual has been in residential care elsewhere. As the deaths of their close relatives occur, residents of centralised facilities lose their connections to localities and become regarded as stateless. Developing services need a fair way of deciding for whom they are responsible and for whom they are not. This is important if the geographic, uneven distribution of resources in the current institution-based service is not to be repeated. Eligibility for 10 Summerton Road was determined by the address of individuals' next-of-kin. Carol was considered eligible by virtue of the address of her brother, who became her next-of-kin when her mother died. She was lucky that he still lived near to the old family address. Otherwise she may never have returned to Merton.

Until there are comprehensive and adequate local services to meet the needs of people with mental handicaps, dislocation of individuals from their familiar surroundings is likely to continue to occur whenever their family or other personal support in the community breaks down. It is some indication of the dependency of such individuals on others and the limitations of present-day services that, when hospital admission was required for her mother, Carol too had to assume the same status. Her mother was old, and in time died. Carol was not old; but departure from her home town had some similarity to death — it was equally sudden and unplanned and could easily have been just as final. After her return, casual acquaintances who knew Carol during the period when she lived with her mother greeted her with statements akin to, "My God, I thought you had died".

It is of course true that citizens do choose to uproot themselves and move periodically. But this fact should not be equated with, and used to excuse, an enforced move necessitated by service inadequacy. Ordinary citizens in general find it relatively easy to re-establish in their new surroundings the kind of casual acquaintanceships they had previously, but this should not lead to the view that the same will be true of someone with a severe mental handicap. The local contacts which Carol has now stem from a time when she was part of a family group, sharing and inheriting the goodwill generated towards the family as a whole. It would be quite a different proposition for her to establish a similar range of contacts elsewhere, independent of family members and absolutely in her own right.

Personal characteristics

Although Carol was admitted to residential care when her family support arrangements broke down, it would be wrong to view her as being totally dependent on others. In areas of her own care she was fairly self-reliant: eating with a knife and fork, fully ambulant, taking herself to the toilet, and washing her face and hands. She could also dress herself fairly well and had some well-formed, clearly articulated, spoken language. Just before her admission to residential care, it is likely that Carol was contributing as much as her mother to their mutual ability to look after themselves. Her language is a considerable asset. Occasionally she has interactions which appear to demonstrate a sophisticated understanding of the world and which follow appropriate social manners. While at the cinema recently, for example, during the intermission Carol and a member of staff were talking about whether or not to queue for ice-creams. A man in the row behind returned from going to the foyer to buy a hot-dog. Carol turned as he approached and said cheerily, "That looks good, how much are they charging for them?". The man told her the price, at which Carol said, "Yeah, it's a rip-off isn't it?". The man agreed, smiled, and resumed his seat while Carol turned back to talk to her companion. The view of the staff member was that it was unlikely that the man realised he had just had a casual conversation with someone with a severe mental handicap.

However, Carol is correctly regarded as someone in the mid-range of the category defined by the term severe mental handicap; she had an assessed mental age of 48 months. In order to convey an accurate picture of her need for support it is necessary to give an accurate picture of her comprehension and use of language. Her capabilities made her just eligible to attend the main workshop of the local adult training centre. Her language ability needs careful evaluation: to some extent it is illusory; the standard of syntax and delivery not being matched by the content and meaning. Her speech is often a collection of short, disjointed phrases and the information it contains is often inaccurate. She finds it difficult to answer questions meaningfully. Conversations often involve repetitive, "cocktail" chatter, based more on formula and social convention than actual comprehension. She is someone who has great personal strengths of enthusiasm, kindness, and sociability. She is also someone for whom it is difficult to encapsulate the precise nature of her handicap and therefore determine the best course of action in order to help her.

The changes in Carol's life on moving to 10 Summerton Road cannot be described in such dramatic terms as those for Shirley, Catherine, or Mary. Nor do they involve such tangible issues. For instance, she did not have a major disruptive behaviour to be coped with, she has not had a job since moving, she did not move from an obviously deprived place of care. Her skills have developed to some extent since moving, but such development is relatively insignificant. The greatest change has been in the breadth of application of the skills she does possess and in the independence with which she leads her life; the flowering of an adult life style.

We hope this feeling of growing maturity and adult independence will come out of our account of Carol's experience of the service. We have had difficulty in striking the right note, given the enigmatic quality of her abilities and handicap. Progress in some areas has been slow. In others advances have been rapid but, even so, we do not wish to represent her development as being less of a challenge to service programming than it has been. Indeed, the most common error we have made in assessing Carol's needs and devising the day-to-day service contribution appropriate to them has been to overemphasise her ability. In particular, we have often misjudged her ability to comprehend complex language, to carry out anything other than simple, one-step instructions, or to keep concentrating on something without frequent support or interest being shown in what she is doing. This is not a criticism of Carol but a representation of the difficulties that we, the service providers, have experienced.

Before moving back

Carol had been admitted to a 25-place facility situated on the corner of a geriatric hospital site on the outskirts of a town. It was a modern building which, apart from its size, was designed to emulate a domestic situation. Bedrooms were single or shared (up to three beds per room), many with washbasins set between the built-in cupboards and wardrobes. There were two living rooms, a large dining room, a hobbies room, and a kitchen (although this had not been fully equipped and meals were supplied from the neighbouring hospital). The unit was comfortably furnished and carpeted and in good decorative order.

It was a difficult time for Carol. She had experienced a major change in her life, possibly with little preparation. She took a long time to settle. She had, and still has, a tendency towards immature social behaviour: making crying noises, being overly apologetic, and sometimes mildly biting her forearm when corrected, however gently or pleasantly. She sought attention and demanded physical contact by asking to be cuddled. She did not want to go on trips out during the first three or four months, although this later became a favourite activity.

One of Carol's great strengths is that she offers her friendship easily and trusts those who respond in kind. She has great sociability and cheerfulness. Although sometimes annoying in her desire for attention, she is so outgoing and pleasant that she is generally well-liked. She is without malice; caring and friendly towards the other people with whom she lives. Staff in the residential unit had described her as having a strong maternal attitude towards one woman, who had a profound and multiple handicap, whom she used to help feed, dress, and otherwise look after. She had also taken a special interest in one younger man who was learning a sign language. She spent much time with him, helping him to practise signing.

Carol's self-help skills were described earlier. She could feed herself neatly and well, she could dress independently even to the extent of putting on appropriate clothes for differing weather conditions, although she needed help with choice of clothes and fashion sense. She needed supervision during bathing and reminders in the morning to brush her hair and teeth. She used to go shopping in town with staff. However, because catering was done elsewhere and many other consumable goods came *via* hospital supplies, there were few opportunities to do so for anything other than personal clothing and toiletries. She had a variety of recreational interests. She liked television and music, and enjoyed dancing and going out to the pub. She also liked physical activities and would join in a game of football played on the back lawn and look forward to the trips to sports and amenity centres which were organised. She attended the local adult training centre during the day.

Other means of occupying her time were relatively limited. The unit maintained some emphasis on residents doing domestic activities which directly concerned them, such as tidying their own rooms; an emphasis that was perhaps greater than would typically be found in a hospital ward. However, the involvement of central catering and laundry services and a full domestic staff meant that Carol had fewer opportunities at the residential unit than she would later experience in her new home. She was involved in tidying, dusting, and polishing her room but she needed much prompting and had a very short attention span. Staff found that she needed constant supervision and attention to keep going. Without this she was likely to stop doing the required task and wait for staff to return, perhaps hoovering one spot over and over or standing holding the tin of polish or looking out of the window. She was involved in a cookery class, but although she appeared to have an intellectual appreciation of what to do she had little practical competence. For example, she knew that a tin-opener was used to open a tin, but she could not do this herself.

Concentration was a continual problem in getting Carol to achieve any level of independence. She could set a table for dinner but needed constant instruction, not only about what to do but also to stick at the job. It was often at these times that her immaturity showed most. She would constantly seek approval: "Carol did well, didn't she?"; "Carol's clever"; and she would respond to helpful instruction by crying or other anxious behaviours which she would then correct herself by saying, "Don't be silly, Carol". She enjoyed going to the pub but staff often found her embarrassing company so these visits were to some extent restricted. While out she would again show immature and mildly inappropriate social behaviour, laughing hysterically at no cause, repeatedly apologising, and making crying, anxious noises.

Carol's appearance at this time underwent some change. She had arrived at the residential unit with what staff described as a rather old-fashioned, "frumpy" appearance. She was quite portly and had a wardrobe of dresses which were mainly shapeless shifts of printed cotton, some long, pleated tweed skirts, and a number of cardigans and blouses, all rather dull in colour. She had a plain hairstyle; straight, shoulder-length, and centre-parted. She lost weight after arrival because, perhaps in her distress, she was choosy about her food. Staff made a conscious effort to introduce more shape to her clothing, to style her hair, and to make her look younger. Subsequently, she began to eat well and regained weight but she kept the younger style.

Staff at the unit cannot recall Carol having any family contact herself, although there were discussions between the staff and

Carol's brother once he became her next-of-kin concerning arrangements for the disposition of their mother's property. Carol inherited a substantial sum in her mother's will and an order was made to place her under the guardianship of the Director of Social Services. However, despite being personally wealthy, she had few possessions of her own at the time. Her money only started to be used more extensively for her own welfare after she moved to 10 Summerton Road.

When the opportunity came for Carol to move back to Merton, the senior staff of the residential unit were not enthusiastic. They advised against moving her again in view of the length of time it had taken for her to settle. Carol was consulted, but her tendency to respond to any question by crying coupled with the unreliability of her statements made it very difficult to interpret what her wishes were. As with Shirley, her own preference could not be properly established. Under these circumstances there were some fears about the wisdom of the transfer; but when the move was finally made, predictions of difficulty proved groundless. Carol was happy to return to her home town and she moved into her new home, with its unfamiliar surroundings and staff, without batting an eyelid.

Developing independence and perseverance

Carol moved to 10 Summerton Road during the second week of November, 1981. The description we had been given of her and the way she behaved in her previous home was confirmed by the initial experience in the house. Her speech gave the impression of greater understanding than she had. Carol could follow simple directions but certainly not those which involved two or more parts. For example, if she were asked to get out a mug and a spoon she would do one or the other, but not both. She did not listen to what people said to her, spending her time instead nodding her head and saying "yes", or making anxious noises, or otherwise answering. Although the impression of the social interaction seemed normal, it lacked function. Even immediately after a conversation Carol would often be unable to do what she had been asked or to repeat what she had been told.

Her dressing skills needed some refinement. She could not fasten the clasps on her bra or tie shoe laces and she tended to pull off her buttons and to enlarge button holes when undressing. Attention-seeking, involving immature social overtures, was frequent and Carol has shown bouts of mild self-injury when demands have been made of her: biting her arm or lightly slapping her face. She could not be given the responsiblity for completing an activity and staff support to lengthen her concentration and perseverance had to be carefully programmed. She also had a habit of collecting and hoarding rubbish (ribbons, pieces of paper, and other small items) and she smoked heavily, pestering others for cigarettes as well as smoking her own.

Carol came to Summerton Road at the same time as Shirley, Catherine, and Mary. She neither presented such conspicuous problems as them nor, compared with Shirley and Mary, had she suffered such neglect. She was the most able, least disruptive, person then living in the house and in the first few months her needs were perhaps made subordinate to those of the others in terms of receiving staff attention. Some things were done for her, but the intensity of effort was missing. Carol had previously held an adult training centre place elsewhere in the county and an application to go to a similar form of day provision was made. She gained a place within the first six months and the main elements of her daily and weekly round resumed a fairly familiar pattern. At one time Carol had smoked heavily but while at the residential unit this had been reduced from up to sixty cigarettes a day to less than five, and then to a couple. This had led to a tendency for her to ask for or otherwise scrounge cigarettes from others. After moving to Summerton Road, she increased her smoking out of personal choice and grew used to offering and accepting offers of cigarettes with staff who smoked. Care was taken that her smoking stayed within reasonable bounds — about ten a day.

Carol now is a smart and presentable woman in late middle-age. She is slim (for her age), has good, well-styled hair, and an attractive face and figure. She has no observable physical signs of handicap, awkwardness of movement, or peculiar mannerisms. Some conscious changes in her appearance have been made since Carol first moved in. The attempt to change her "old fashioned" appearance which had been made in her previous place of care had resulted in an appearance more suited to a juvenile than an up-to-date adult. Immature appearance is common among adults with mental handicaps and it can have the effect of accentuating their intellectual disability through the sense of childishness and lack of responsibility it conveys. This was particularly unfortunate for Carol who, despite a beneficial physical appearance, was in danger of being seen as genuinely immature because of her social behaviour. The need for her to develop a more mature bearing and physical appearance, as well as improved social behaviour, were soon identified as prime objectives.

In common with the other people moving to the house, a process of purchasing new clothes, adult shoes, and jewellery, of having new and changing hairstyles, and of experimenting with make-up and other cosmetics to enhance appearance was begun. Carol had the added advantage of personal wealth held under the guardianship arrangement. In order to buy clothes and other possessions, negotiations were conducted on Carol's behalf so that she could have greater access to her money. She began to receive a regular income with occasional larger amounts for expenditure on consumer durables. After eighteen months, the guardianship arrangements were relinquished and her money is now held in trust. This provides appropriate controls while easing the practicalities of gaining access to her income. Carol has her own Post Office account which she uses both to finance day-to-day requirements and to save for items involving more substantial expenditure. As a consequence she now has a large wardrobe of both work-a-day and high quality clothes. Probably of all the people who live in the house, she is the only one who could be described as possessing a wardrobe of clothes suitable for all of the normal range of social functions that a successful working member of the community might attend. She can dress suitably for the theatre or for a London show or to go to church; events which she attends regularly as part of the community life style of a person with resources.

The rearrangement of her financial matters has altered Carol's status of having few possessions. She now owns a range of material goods from which she can derive pleasure. Her spending, following staff recommendations on her behalf, is certainly not profligate. She has bought a television and some stereo equipment for her own room, she has been able to change some of her room furnishings so that they are more to her taste, her choice of holiday is generally less constrained than it is for her companions, and she is able to go to a wider range of cultural events as she can afford the cost of travel away from Merton more often than others with a lesser income.

The objective of developing a social demeanour appropriate to a smart woman in her fifties has been a more complex matter to attain. Teaching and changing behaviour is more difficult than buying new clothes! But progress to the current position can be traced back to the first weeks in the house. Carol was encouraged to participate more in her own care and in activities about the house. She was also encouraged to be more reserved in social manners, differentiating friends from strangers in the style of greeting, and desisting from intimate hugging or kissing. (The frequency of contact from relatives has remained low and there are few people in Carol's life for whom such intimate interactions are appropriate.) Another objective was to reduce the crying, overly apologetic, sometimes self-injurious, or otherwise immature or inappropriate reactions to requests, correction, or criticism. In using the word correction here, we are not talking about punishment. We mean help and support to do something correctly and successfully. An inability to accept the help and advice of others is a considerable barrier to achieving a more normal social existence and developing independence.

The other side of the coin was for Carol not only to develop new skills but also to use the ones she possessed to gain more independent control over her activities. If she could develop perseverance in tasks she could do, and take initiatives that would lead to genuine accomplishment, her contribution would naturally generate the social recognition she so obviously wanted. Participation and accomplishment were seen as more constructive, alternative ways of gaining staff attention than the immature and anxious behaviours she displayed. These were ambitious, global objectives, and in some respects development has been slow. Sometimes staff effort has had little return; nevertheless, the definition of Carol's major needs has been successful on the whole in giving the service a therapeutic direction which has promoted significant changes in Carol's status, personal confidence, and life style. Although changes in different areas overlap and interact with each other, for ease of description Carol's progress will be described under three headings: her contribution to the household; her independence as a "lady about town"; and her growing social maturity as an adult.

Being a contributing household member

Carol was always one of the most substantial contributors to household life. When working with her staff had the sense that the task of getting something done could be taken at a slightly more casual level. The change over time is in the quality of how she fulfils her role. She is now considerably more skilled, more mature, and more confident, so she is treated as being more responsible. Her rate of learning has not been as dramatic as Shirley's who, despite her absence of language, has also assumed a particularly responsible position in the household. Nor was it achieved so easily. Carol has an enigmatic quality; an ability to appear to know how to do something because she can respond, in a transient fashion, to requests. But unlike Shirley she has a substantial functional handicap in not being able to perform the mechanics of the tasks she sets out to do. She lacks any sense of standard and she tends to start an activity without being able to carry it through. A consistent mistake in the service staff's response to her has been to overestimate her ability; a mistake which was never in Carol's interests. Experience in the last three years has been of an ultimately rewarding but painstaking job: showing Carol how to do all the everyday range of domestic tasks; giving her instruction and, initially, frequent praise to motivate participation; then gradually reducing the frequency of praise in order to lengthen her concentration and build accomplishment.

Carol, as a result, has learned to make simple meals, to clean, tidy, polish, make drinks, iron clothing, wash up, stack the dishwasher, unpack the shopping and put things away, and do the laundry (with some continuing help and supervision). Her attention to tasks and her perseverance has gradually increased so that she is now able to continue tasks for about twenty minutes or so, quite long enough for the deliberately programmed praise and encouragement to give way to that recognition and social interaction we all get as an incidental consequence of our activity. It would be nice to be able to say that the programme staff followed to gain this development was so precise that what emerged was a gradual but constant growth in competence, desire to join in, and increase in concentration in the classic manner. The truth is a little wider of the mark.

A recurrent mistake has been to misjudge the length of time Carol can continue an activity without encouragement. Often, because of the need to pay attention to a member of the household who is more severely handicapped, by the time attention has been given back to Carol she has either ceased to be engaged in her task or has left it completely to seek out staff in order to gain attention some other way (often by displaying immature social behaviours or by complaining of aches, pains, or invented injuries). When the balance of staff attention has moved away from being directed at constructive engagement in a meaningful activity, it has invariably shifted to those behaviours which Carol has initiated, presumably because she has found them to bring about long-standing success in gaining attention, namely: complaining, crying, irrational laughter, mild hypochondria and "acting silly." However, we think it is also true to say that one of the strengths of this residential service has been the sensitivity of its staff to subtle changes in behavioural frequency shown by the people living in the house and their ability to analyse these and adjust their own performance within the structure of the weekly staff meetings. Fluctuating behaviour is not seen as the random variation inherent in the expression of an individual's underlying personality trait. Instead it is viewed as a possible rational comment by the individual on the prevailing situation. Thus, perhaps in a more faltering fashion than would be ideal, the pattern of staff interaction with Carol has largely met her needs and enabled progress to continue.

Carol now knows how to collect what she needs for a bath, run the bath water, take a bath, wash herself adequately, and dry herself afterwards. She has become consistently competent in self-care after using the toilet. She has learned to brush her hair thoroughly and to maintain her hairstyle, and she is making progress in her ability to wash her hair herself. She now brushes her teeth regularly with an electric toothbrush. Specific teaching has been given for some of the more subtle refinements in dressing and undressing, and attention has been given to detail, such as teaching Carol to wash and dry her hands thoroughly after finishing working in the kitchen.

But more important than the increments in specific skills is Carol's heightened motivation to engage in activity and contribute to the household. This is beginning to generate a degree of self-initiated activity which, though not as sophisticated as that shown by Shirley, is still to be cherished. It is evidence of a step being taken which provides a degree of optimism for further development. It also reflects a certain quality about the ethos of the house: that the people who live in it feel free to take upon themselves the decision to do something. Carol will initiate the making of a cup of tea or coffee for herself or the household. She likes gardening, has become good at it, and chooses when to go out and do it. She is becoming reliable at tidying her room in the morning before going to the adult training centre. She initiates cleaning and polishing of the furniture, and doing the laundry. She still needs staff help to carry out the entire sequence of activities involved in performing these tasks, and the standard of cleaning and polishing benefits from staff guidance, but these are relatively minor points. Carol can iron clothes completely independently and will sometimes decide to occupy herself in this way for twenty minutes to half-an-hour at a stretch. She likes shopping and can unpack and put away the goods she has bought.

Being a lady about town

Independence in life has also been developed for Carol in her use of the surrounding community. Carol is sociable in nature, knows her local town well, and is in turn familiar to a considerable number of local inhabitants. She enjoys going to the shops or to activities in the evening. She has no close contacts or substantial friendships other than her brother's family (whom she sees little) and a cousin (whom she refers to as "Aunt") and her husband who live in a town in the neighbouring county. She goes to stay with them about six times a year. Being a fairly active member of a local community, with a network of casual acquaintances, may partially offset the absence of any close relationships and give her a real sense of belonging.

To enhance Carol's ability to benefit from her return to Merton, various specific skills relevant to independent or accompanied use of local community facilities have been taught over the last three years. At her first individual programme planning meeting in 1982 road drill was identified as an area for development, although little concerted effort in this respect was made until a year later. When programming did start, Carol was first taught simply to look for and identify the arrival of the training centre transport at the house in the morning. Later she was taught to halt at a kerb without a reminder, then to decide when to cross side roads, and afterwards how to cross the main road at a place with a central island. She began to catch the town bus to go to the adult training centre instead of using the supplied transport. At first she had staff help, and then some supervision from one of the trainees from the centre which was organised by staff. Involvement of this trainee was not altogether successful and a move to the final step of travelling independently was somewhat accelerated out of necessity. At this point, when Carol was leaving the house alone to cross the road, go to the bus-stop, and catch the bus, and doing the reverse on return, staff kept a concealed watch to make sure that she had learned the necessary skills to negotiate the journey independently and safely. Once satisfied of this, Carol has been able to travel unaided.

Apart from crossing roads and using a bus, other teaching for Carol has centred on queuing and turn-taking in shops and in the Post Office where she has her account, holding shop doors open for the convenience of others, closing a car door after getting out without a reminder, and using a seat-belt also without a reminder. Although not good at money she can now name some coins and can use the closest shops (a greengrocers and a newsagents) independently, either taking a list and sufficient money for household shopping or asking the assistant and managing payment herself for specific items such as cigarettes. In a supermarket she can find goods on request provided only one instruction is given at a time. She has also learned to order drinks in a pub.

These skills are adding a considerable dimension to Carol's life of independent action outside the house. The safe crossing of roads and use of the bus, which had first been achieved for the specific journey to and from the training centre, has generalised to other roads and use of other bus-stops. For example, rather than always getting off at the stop nearest the house when returning from the training centre, Carol may choose to travel directly to town to look around the shops, and to walk home afterwards. Moreover, to complement their growing responsibility for their own safety outside the house, it has recently been decided that Carol and Shirley may be left alone inside the house for short periods. This means that the choice of activity available for all the people who live at 10 Summerton Road is becoming less interdependent and less constrained by staff availability. For Shirley and Carol this development is very similar to what happens when a teenager becomes independent from the requirement to accompany the family every time the household shopping needs to be done or when a younger brother or sister has to be taken to an appointment outside the house.

Growing social maturity

Carol's growing social maturity is essential to her independent use of community facilities. Without it, and the resultant responsibility she shows for her actions, the independence she is permitted would not be possible. It would be tempting to view this development as a natural by-product of a greater access to the normal adult social world, either through some improvement in self-image, or through direct exposure to competent role models, or through some conditioning process inherent in the reactions of other citizens within the community. Certainly, opportunity to develop is a pre-requisite for development and the opportunity to imitate competent citizens can only help this process. It is also beneficial when other citizens respond appropriately and with understanding to an individual's social overtures. But to attribute change exclusively to such factors would be to ignore the planned and coordinated staff management that has occurred.

Although it can still not be claimed that Carol has the maturity expected of a woman in her fifties, much of her immature social behaviour has lessened in frequency and intensity, to the extent that it is now rare. For example, she now has perfectly passable social behaviour in a pub: she can sit and converse in a discreet enough manner, she can order drinks, she can take turns, she can play fruit machines without direct guidance and without making a silly pretence of hopelessness. She can go to the cinema (accompanied) and behave in a way which causes no concern and is completely acceptable to other members of the audience. She is able to go to concerts and on other trips out. Her demeanour within the house is similarly improved.

In developing her social abilities, staff have always had an advantageous starting point in terms of Carol's inherent sociability, cheerfulness, cooperativeness, and desire to please. What needed to be changed was the way in which she attracted the attentions of others, from one which portrayed her as a somewhat embarrassing spectacle, playing on characteristics associated with handicap and immaturity, to one which emphasised her competence and achievement. Her ability to accomplish worthwhile tasks in the house, which was fostered by teaching her new skills and greater perseverance by means of a mixture of staff instruction and deliberate attention to worthwhile activity, was the general backdrop to changes in her interpersonal behaviour. Over-intimate greeting, hugging, and kissing was discouraged in much the same way as it had been for the much more extreme form shown by Mary. Reduction of false crying and invention of complaints was achieved by encouraging her to persevere with alternative forms of occupation and by giving her due recognition when she followed instructions and engaged in worthwhile activity. At the same time staff simply asked Carol not to cry, complain, or "act silly," and not to apologise repeatedly following correction. If she persisted, they ignored her.

Progress was not uniformly good; there were periodic setbacks. The most significant occurred after about two years in the house when Carol began to show an increasing frequency of mildly self-injurious behaviour which took the form of biting her forearm and slapping her face. Staff collected information on its frequency, the antecedents to the behaviour, and the consequences that followed. The data indicated that Carol injured herself when staff asked her to do things, despite the fact that they usually continued to require her to do what they had asked and ensured that she did so. Probably two factors were associated with the behaviour. First, the self-injury deflected the demand for a few seconds, thus delaying the need to make a response. Second, it probably had the effect on staff of offering Carol more help when they repeated their request. The recurrent problem of over-rating Carol's abilities and expecting too much of her had been found again.

The response to this episode was finally a good one, both for the specific problem and for Carol's social behaviour in general. It seemed to mark a real breakthrough in her developing maturity and a change in the relationship between Carol and the staff. Carol was taught to ask for help. For incidents of hitting herself, complaining, "acting silly," or crying, she was given a short reprimand and then instructed to say, "Can you help me please?", or words to that effect. Staff persistence with teaching her to ask for help in an adult manner was successful. Carol's more immature forms of avoiding demands or gaining help started to lessen and she grew in status in the eyes of the staff.

A woman about the house

As Carol has grown more mature in her manner, it is possible to trace changes in the relationship between her and the staff. There has been a greater relaxation in the style of interaction which is now closer to that of a peer-group friendship than before. As has been said, her more mature status is reflected in the decision that she can be left with Shirley in the house unsupervised. She can take decisions on her own initiative. One story concerns an incoming telephone call. After dinner, the telephone rang when staff and some of the household were washing-up in the kitchen and Carol was clearing the dining room. Carol called, "I'll go" and answered the 'phone. Staff heard the typical listener's response of a periodic "Yes", "Uh, hum", and then Carol said, "I'll get her" and put the receiver down beside the 'phone. Carol found Linda (another member of the household) and said, "'Phone, it's for you", and Linda went to the 'phone to take a call from her mother. The entire episode was appropriately conducted without any staff intervention. It illustrates how people living in the house can assume increasing responsibility in their own home environment.

Carol has little contact from relatives; maybe one or two visits a year from her brother's family. Mollie (her cousin who looked after Carol's mother during her later years) and her husband Ken invite Carol to stay with them for the week-end every other month or so. But otherwise Carol's life is based essentially within her house and in her town. She did develop a friendship at the adult training centre with a woman of about her own age who lives in a hostel some twelve miles distant and invited her to stay at the house overnight on several occasions, but that friendship has since declined. Within the house, Carol has moved from having her own room to sharing with Kathleen, who moved in two years after her. Kath, as she likes to be called, is a bit younger, attends the training centre and, until about a year ago, lived at home with her mother. Kath had previously spent several short stays at the house and objectives had been set in both women's individual programme planning meetings which would foster their friendship for their mutual benefit; Carol being rather short of close contacts, and Kath being rather isolated at home from any involvement in the local community, particularly in the evening. When Carol went to the cinema or a concert locally (accompanied by staff), she began to call for Kath on the way. After Kath moved to the house, Carol chose to share a double room with her.

Carol has the kind of daily and weekly routine that adults in ordinary families look forward to having after their children have grown up. On weekdays she has to get up at about 7.30 am to get ready to go to work (at the training centre). She likes to have breakfast TV on as she wakes up, washes (there is a vanitory unit in her bedroom), and gets dressed. At weekends she gets up later, between 9.00 and 10.00 am., and likes to watch TV in bed. She usually goes to bed about midnight, although she can go earlier if she feels tired. On Friday and Saturday evenings she might watch the late film. When cleaning and tidying her room, or when changing to go out in the evening, she often listens to the radio, a record, or a tape. At other times she might not choose to watch TV or listen to her stereo in her own room, preferring to be part of the social group in the house. In the evenings she might go to a pub or to the cinema, or she may decide to stay in and have a bath. Sometimes she may need to attend to housework or take her share in doing the main shopping for the household. (This is usually done at a supermarket which stays open late on some evenings during the week.) She is a keen gardener and has taken on the front garden as her own to tend and develop.

Throughout more than three years at the house, the individual programme planning approach has ensured that staff regularly review their thinking about what is best for Carol's welfare. Attention has been paid to some very specific things: teaching her to sit in a skirt with her knees close together rather than sprawled apart, particularly when out at the pub; and teaching her how to use her television and music centre without any help. Other things have been more general: concerned with her health, appearance, and role in society. For example, Carol and a member of staff regularly attend an evening keep-fit class run for the general public. Recently Carol has had partial dentures to fill the gaps between her natural teeth and these have been a great success. Although she initially said she would not wear them she now willingly uses them all the time.

One major issue for the future is for Carol to obtain a more productive and rewarding working life. As the burden on staff time from supporting Shirley in her job eases (see Chapter 2), it may be possible to carry out a similar exercise for Carol. Staff may be able to establish a similar co-worker arrangement, but in a different type of job — one which is more suitable for someone with a sociable personality like Carol's — and then gradually to withdraw their support after having taught Carol independent competence. There is a possibility that Carol will be a productive wage earner before she reaches retirement age.

Although her family is not a close one, Carol is still part of it. Both her cousin and her brother have been impressed by the changes that have occurred, in particular the growth of Carol's sense of self-reliance, responsibility, and social maturity Carol now has her name on the council house waiting list. Who knows what the future might bring?

CHAPTER 6

Richard Oliver, Margaret Tarrant, Elizabeth Shaw, Kathleen Wright — a variety of issues

We have given a full account in the preceding chapters of the changes for four people in order to illustrate how attention to a wide range of quality considerations can be coordinated to take account of individual needs. For Richard, Margaret, Elizabeth, and Kathleen we intend to highlight just one or two of the major issues relating to their involvement with 10 Summerton Road; selecting some of the key elements in what coming to live there has meant for them, rather than giving a comprehensive description.

Richard Oliver: even if it is a higher quality service, it is still the only choice

In highlighting the advantages over what has gone before, it is easy to get perilously close to arguing that the new alternative is undoubtedly the best. We need to avoid falling into this trap. It is still the case that the usual service response to someone who requires additional help to live an adequate home life is the offer of a place in a group residential setting rather than an attempt to provide supportive arrangements in the person's home situation. People with mental handicaps, whether they are offered a high or poor quality option, tend not to have a real choice between alternatives; only the ability to accept or refuse the service offered.

Richard Oliver lived in 10 Summerton Road for just five months. His story illustrates the straight-jacket of service response; something which even small housing developments do not change. 10 Summerton Road, although smaller than most, is still a group setting. The service emphasis is still on the provision of a single building by which the needs of several people are to be met. It does not respond by designing the optimal residential service arrangement as needed by each person individually. Of its type, the house might be considered to be an example of a high quality facility; but there are limitations that should be recognised concerning what such a type of facility can achieve. The people who come to live at 10 Summerton Road are moved from where they lived before, away from the very local ties they may have had, into a service building, the nature and location of which remains permanent and unchanging even though the individuals it serves change from time to time as do the staff who care for them.

Richard transferred to 10 Summerton Road from a small mental handicap hospital in a converted Victorian workhouse in November 1982, twelve months after the house opened. Although he was elderly, sixty-seven years old, he had only been admitted to residential care at the age of sixty-five; indeed that was the first time he had been diagnosed as having a severe mental handicap. His presenting problem in contacting the health services was a serious skin complaint. As a result he was diagnosed as having Down's syndrome and transferred into the mental handicap hospital services.

Richard had spent his life in one of the small villages near Merton. There his family owned land and derived income from it. Richard lived within the family set-up and performed a useful role, helping in a simple way with the agricultural work, for example, leading and tending the horses. Despite the fact that Richard had Down's syndrome, perhaps the most identifiable set of physiological signs most consistently indicative of severe intellectual impairment, it had never been recognised that he was mentally handicapped. He was known to be deaf and therefore an explanation existed for his lack of language; his slowness in other ways and his refusal to do what might be asked of him was put down to stubbornness, allied to a degree of simple-mindedness. When he was in his sixties, Richard had a bad occurrence of dermatitis which was allowed to gain hold over his entire body. This caused serious flaking of the skin and soreness, particularly on his face, fingers, and feet. He was admitted to the acute hospital for treatment where he was identified as having a severe mental handicap and, as a dramatic example of rigid categorisation, transferred to the mental handicap hospital sector.

There are a number of remarkable facets in Richard's story. Firstly, the fact that he had spent sixty years of his life, albeit in a tranquil rural backwater, without being labelled severely mentally handicapped, illustrates well that notions of handicap are not absolute but relative to particular social situations. Secondly, in marked contrast, the acute health services responded as if the mental handicap rather than the skin complaint was the paramount concern. Thirdly, it illustrates that former workhouses and other large, old-fashioned institutions, which were brought into the National Health Service and titled "hospitals" on its foundation, have become accepted as a source of specialist services despite the manifest shortage of a variety of resources, including those as basic as an adequate physical environment and a reasonable proportion of trained staff. Of course it may be convenient in some quarters not to look beyond the veneer of the official title. There is often open recognition of the inadequacies of the long-stay mental handicap institutions. But at the same time, the use of vague terms such as "hospital" in phrases such as "the need for hospital care" can conjure an impression of high standards of health care delivery which are specially designed for people with mental handicaps and are, therefore, better than those that could be obtained from generic community services. Our experience as set out in the earlier chapters, and from past research, shows the reality is somewhat different. We become too concerned with inventing categories by which to pigeon-hole people and titles for services to match the categories. In the case of Richard, our own involvement in the small home service was not free from this fault.

Richard suddenly found himself in a poorly staffed and old-fashioned facility for men with mental handicaps, on the edge of a village on the other side of the health district in which he lived; a victim of inter-consultant referral. The skin complaint was not the only contributing factor to his situation. He was growing old, parental support was no longer available, and his elder sister with whom he lived was beginning to have more difficulty in managing. But the laziness of the service response should also be seen as possibly the primary contributing factor. When members of the responsible mental handicap services management team other than the psychiatrist were alerted to his situation, they responded to the inappropriateness of Richard's placement. But ultimately the service failed to respond well to the needs of either Richard or his immediate family. Had the route into service involvement been other than that which occurred, it might have been possible to replace or add to the family support which had allowed Richard to be a member of a village community all his life. As it was, he embarked on a new home life in his retirement.

The institution to which Richard was sent was designed in the last century as an ideal environment in which to supervise the provision of cold comfort for the destitute and other disadvantaged people. Despite conspicuous efforts by the district health authority which inherited its management in 1974 to revamp this environment, it still retained much of its original character. It was arranged in three ward blocks on three sides of a central quadrangle. These three wards at one time housed up to eighty-six men, but numbers have been actively reduced in the last few years. Accommodation was rudimentary — large rectangular dormitories, large day-rooms with chairs in ranks, and a single, separate dining room for the entire facility. Toileting and washing facilities were similar to those in public buildings. Some attempts had been made in recent years to provide better accommodation, for example, by converting the chapel and surrounding small rooms into a self-sufficient flat for the benefit of a few of the residents. But such changes could only have a marginal effect. The overwhelming impression was of a barren environment, exemplified by the fact that the internal walls were painted, unplastered brickwork. Some of the staff were aware of today's more progressive philosophies, involving encouraging residents' independence and participation in community life. However, although staff tried to encourage some of the residents to visit pubs in the village, the village was too small and too smart to be able to cope with so many, rather bedraggled, institutional residents. There was no disguising the fact that these people were, in all senses of the term, on the edge of society.

Richard had remained in this facility rather than 10 Summerton Road, which was at least local to his previous address, because he was not at first considered to be sufficiently handicapped to merit the intensively staffed health service contribution to the comprehensive range of community services, which was how this new house was defined. In other words, Richard did not fit the category which was used to decide who would be offered this improved service. This kind of rigidity is inherent when service provision is so inadequate that judgements about who can and who cannot receive it have to be made.

Richard moved to 10 Summerton Road following a reassessment of his abilities and a change in opinion: he was considered to fit the eligibility criteria after all. He had at first been assessed as being able to eat, wash, and dress independently in the institutional setting, and to be fully ambulant with no behaviour disorder. It was, therefore, felt that responsibility lay with the local authority social services department to make suitable local provision for him. However, the early assessment was misleading. For example, Richard's ability to dress himself fully was dependent on a supply of loose-fitting clothing and elasticated trousers. He was very deaf and had no spoken language. Deemed to be eligible for 10 Summerton Road after all, he became the fifth person to move into the house on a permanent basis.

Making the best of a bad job

Richard only lived in the house for five months. At the age of sixty-seven he stumbled and fell, breaking his femur. Surgeons decided to operate and pin the bone. Richard died twenty-four hours after coming round from the anaesthetic. There was some speculation afterwards that he may have had a congenital heart defect. Our knowledge of his previous family life is sketchy as we only knew him and his family for a short time. But it can probably be said with a fair degree of confidence that life for Richard, even in the unusually enriched and progressive form of residential care provided at Summerton Road, was a second-best solution compared to his continuing to live to the end of his days among the family and circumstances he had always known.

It is hard to imagine what the impact on Richard was in moving from his family home to a mental handicap institution. In terms of personal ability and personality he probably remained relatively unchanged, being much the same in terms of skills and interests as he was when he later moved back to Merton. We are confronted again in Richard's story, as in other people's stories, by the fact that a person's life style, daily living opportunities, and membership of an identifiable community, are not wholly dependent on that individual's abilities, even where the person is considered mentally handicapped. It is not the mental handicap that causes the life style, the lack of opportunity, or the separation from the mainstream of society that can be occasioned by admission to a residential service. These are shaped to a considerable extent by the characteristics of the service provision itself.

In the short time that Richard lived at 10 Summerton Road no-one would claim that substantial development of his personal skills occurred. However, his life style was able to be changed back to something closer to what he may have previously experienced: a person living with help in an ordinary house within a local community. Richard's reversal of fortune points to a general lesson that must be learned in considering the residential placement of people with mental handicaps. Those individuals currently living in institutions do not necessarily have to be habilitated, that is, taught to be more able, *before* they can learn to live in community settings. Rather, community settings should be arranged to support such individuals, given the skills, interests, and personalities they currently possess.

Richard was of retirement age, was slow, and a little frail. He was ambulant, continent (with a few accidents), and able to dress himself if given help with fastenings. His fine manipulation finger control was not good and his ability to grip strongly was badly affected by the soreness caused by the skin complaint which was still causing him trouble. He was sociable, could understand speech if it were accompanied by gestural communication, but had no words himself or understanding of a formal sign language. He wore hearing aids in both ears. He appeared to be used to a traditionally male domestic role — sitting and waiting to be served his meals and drinks. He smoked heavily and liked a drink of beer. His skin complaint remained unchecked despite the considerable time that he had spent in the mental handicap hospital. Rather than seeking further advice to clear the condition, treatment there had been for him to wear white cotton gloves.

For Richard the main contribution of the local housing service was to embark in the direction of re-establishing his community and family ties, establishing a useful role for him in retirement within the house, and meeting his basic needs effectively. Thus his hearing was checked and hearing aids adjusted, spectacles were obtained, and treatment of the skin condition was assiduously followed. When consistent application of the lotions did not bring improvement within a short period of time, a second consultation was obtained with the original specialist. A changed régime of treatment was prescribed and followed and the condition cleared up. Moreover, Richard's personal appearance was generally improved from that which was tolerated in the mental handicap hospital. New clothing was obtained, much bought and supplied by his family, and care was taken over presentability: his trousers were kept pressed, shirts which required it were starched and ironed, and he wore a neck tie. During his first week after moving in, chiropody treatment was started. With a similar urgency, his dentures were checked and new ones obtained. To be perfectly honest, no-one was quite sure whether he transferred from the mental handicap hospital with his own or someone else's false teeth!

Richard's sister, niece, and more extended family were very pleased that he was able to live locally. They were keen to be involved and to make sure that his interests were served. Richard was half-owner of a caravan park and his family were in full collaboration with the service to arrange a regular income so that he could enjoy the advantages of such a position. Family members visited the house, and service staff arranged for Richard to visit his sister weekly for lunch. About the time of his death, arrangements were being made for Richard to join the active old people's club in his old village, of which his sister was a member. As a retired man, Richard was a regular visitor to town, often accompanied by Mary who, like him, had no alternative day-time occupation. He shopped and went to the pub for a beer; he continued to smoke cigarettes.

Within the house, Richard began to develop much more active participation in home life. For him, it was probably a new role. He gave every impression that in his family life housework had been for women. However, he rapidly began to enjoy many routine domestic tasks: stacking and unloading the dishwasher, putting crockery, cutlery, and shopping away, simple dusting and hoovering, peeling and slicing vegetables. He worked collaboratively with other people, such as Carol or Shirley, obviously responsive to their company and attempting to communicate by means of rudimentary sign language. Teaching of a formal sign language was begun, but there was insufficient time to make substantial progress.

Margaret Tarrant: release from institutional squalor

Two themes are emphasised in Margaret's story: the comparison of her previous institutional environment with that of the small home; and the views of her mother on both. Margaret became a boarder at a Rudolph Steiner School at the age of eleven-and-a-half, but sadly her behaviour in just six weeks proved too difficult. Unfortunately, no other suitable school could be found for her, so Margaret was admitted to a long-stay mental handicap hospital. As a young adult she had lived on the female locked ward of that hospital. She therefore had lived among people considered to be disturbed, viewed as beyond hope; people to be confined on the "back ward" away from not only ordinary community life but also the already segregated society of the remainder of the hospital. Fortunately for Margaret, her family moved into the catchment area of 10 Summerton Road and about eighteen months after the house had opened she was able to leave the institution, never to return.

In order to place the following description in context, we must honestly say that the ward on which Margaret was living is one of the most dehumanising, blatantly awful situations in which human beings live that we have ever seen. Not all mental handicap hospital wards are so poor. We have seen many better; but we have also seen worse, and others just as bad. We think it chastening to give a short, frank description of the impression of that ward as a challenge to the view that such conditions are a thing of the past, eradicated by the priority status that has supposedly been given to mental handicap throughout the last two decades. Our comparison with other wards which have better conditions is current and so too is our comparison with hospital wards which are worse. The ward where Margaret lived is not a rare relic of the past.

What a "locked ward" is in practice varies. In some cases it means that the external doors are kept locked and residents come and go only with staff mediation. In other cases it is simply an archaic term for a hospital ward where all the "difficult cases" end up and does not reflect an actual policy of locking doors. In others, and this was the case where Margaret lived, the emphasis on security is far greater, and many internal doors within the building are routinely locked in addition to those leading to the outside.

In Margaret's ward, residents were collected and effectively penned during the day in the living room. Access to the rest of the ward was denied by locking doors to all other areas. When not in use the dining room, bathrooms, and bedrooms were also kept locked. The staff office, always locked when not in use, was even locked sometimes when staff occupied the room. Only staff had keys; keys were never left in locks. When the living room and ablution block doors were open, access to and from them was possible. Sometimes the toilets were locked and access was unavailable. However, even when access was available, staff help to assist residents to perform what they required to do was not necessarily available. The care given to even the most basic individual needs — to use a toilet, drink when thirsty, eat when hungry, to have privacy — was minimal. The phenomenon described by other writers about institutional life of "block treatment" — the mass processing of groups of people together — was the mechanism for the dispensing of care. There were toileting times, washing times, mealtimes, dressing and undressing times, and bedtime; the same for everyone — and the requisite living areas were unlocked, used, and re-locked accordingly. Other than through these set routines, care was haphazard, resident initiated, and performed by residents to the best of their limited abilities. If a resident did not use a toilet when urinating, for example, then it was seen as being either because the person had not learned to do so or had learned not to do so; and the service had no structure or ability to guarantee staff presence to alter the situation.

The living room was one of the most unpleasant places in which anyone could wish to pass many hours, let alone every day. It was a large space with a hard, vinyl-tiled floor, separated from the dining room by a wooden "concertina" partition. The rudimentary furnishings comprised some plastic chairs, and some easy chairs typical of modern institutional provision with a wooden frame, webbing straps, and loose vinyl-covered cushions. One corner of the room, where the television was situated, was carpeted. There were some bright orange, vinly-covered sag-bags. There were no materials provided to offer any means of passing the day purposefully occupied. At times, urine and faeces were on the floor; the smell was difficult to bear. When we were there we saw people urinating on the floor and one woman manually taking faeces from her rectum and smearing them on the wall. We do not know whether staff saw the incidents we witnessed but, given that we noticed such occurrences during only a number of short visits, they must have been aware that their service promoted and tolerated such events. One resident displayed a marked problem behaviour: ripping the clothing off other people while they wore it; and several people physically assaulted themselves or others. We do not know whether such actions were seen by the staff on duty and allowed to continue without any attempt at intervention being made.

As far as we could see, the people we saw squatting to urinate in the living room were left unwashed afterwards. Some, no doubt, were sitting in urine-sodden clothing. Others did not have that discomfort as they were in various states of nakedness anyway; either from the waist down or in a complete state of undress. Urine, and sometimes faeces, lay for quite a while on the floor until noticed and removed by staff. It is not surprising the room stank. We once saw a staff member, on seeing a pool of urine on the floor, go and collect a large linen sheet, cover the urine with it and allow it to soak in. She then took the sheet away. No further attempt was made to cleanse or disinfect the floor.

The major form of human interaction in the living room seemed to stem from some residents abusing others: being assaultive, removing or ripping others' clothing, removing others' shoes and throwing them away. In the main people showed extreme social withdrawal. Margaret herself spent long periods curled up on a chair, either holding her head and covering her eyes, or staring into nowhere; or similarly lying on the floor; or pacing up and down, twisting her hair round and round with her one good hand. At times she stopped to hit her jaw or nose with her fist and to shout out. Other people showed similar patterns of repetitive, withdrawn behaviour. One woman filled her day by pacing in a small circle holding one arm vertically in front of her and rotating her hand, helicopter-fashion, in front of her eyes. Another stood with her forehead resting on the wooden partition to the dining room, using it as pivot to allow her to rotate her trunk repetitively in alternating, semi-circular fashion. When we closed our eyes and just listened we could hear no conversation, no excited chatter, no signs of happiness; just sometimes the odd word called out, like "nurse", and mostly a low murmur of moans and whimpering punctuated by an occasional high-pitched scream or bout of screaming.

Toilets and washbasins were in a large ablution block with a marble floor. The toilets themselves were in cubicles; though partitioned, someone of normal adult height could look over the top of the dividers if they chose to do so. In all, the area was like a public lavatory. The half-glazed door to the foyer was usually open. The toilets were on the other side of the foyer from the living room door. There were open drainage gutters under the sinks which, when they were blocked by clothing and the taps were left on, would overflow. There was no toilet paper. The bathrooms were kept locked. They had no luxury or refinement about them in any way; just a free-standing bathtub in the middle of a tiled floor. In the central foyer, just outside the dayroom, a small, half-glazed room had been created. This was used to seclude people who were behaviourally disturbed. We saw a person left in that room, beating herself and screaming, and in the process missing her meal.

Meals were served in the dining room, which was opened for the occasion, and which was the other half of the rectangle that constituted the day-time area of the ward. The food was not prepared on the ward. It came from the central kitchen in a heated trolley, from which it was served onto plastic plates and bowls in a room adjacent to the dining room and then passed through a hatch. Residents waited in chaotic fashion, some sitting, some generally milling about, and some standing at or near the hatch. While waiting for her meal, Margaret sat rocking backwards and forwards in her chair, tapping the front or side of her nose with cutlery. The meal was an unceremonious affair performing no more than the function of providing sustenance to hungry people.

Given this ambience, it is not difficult to imagine the repetitious, unstimulating, wasteful existence Margaret led. Moving to 10 Summerton Road provided a dramatic contrast, a radically different way of life, and a substantially improved role for her to fulfil. The detailed programmes which staff designed and followed in order to teach Margaret small, new competencies do not represent the substance of the major change; being only peripheral niceties in the contrast between her previous existence and her new one. The small home service has set teaching objectives and implemented programmes designed to teach Margaret new skills and to alter socially undesirable ones. Of greatest significance, however, is not the success or failure staff have had in affecting Margaret's behaviour, but in how such effort represents the service orientation. The desire to teach useful functional skills, to improve appearance through gaining elegant and fashionable clothing and hairstyles, and to teach "normal" social behaviour stems from a philosophy of promoting meaning in the life of the person who is handicapped: which culminates in a life of contribution to the running of the household and of involvement in the wider community world.

There are challenges inherent in such aspirations. There is no magical process by which the domestic and community-based characteristics of the new service seep through the pores of the skin of the person who is handicapped and generate in that person ordinary domestic and social skills, preferences, and standards.

Thus, following transfer, Margaret has retained ways of behaving and preferences which were part of her institutional past. She arrived at the house with a long-standing proclivity for holding and carrying objects — a teddy-bear and any small ornament. Her sleep at night is often disturbed; she sometimes wakes in a state of excitement, wanting to walk around, sing, and put paper and clothing down the toilet. She has thrown toilet paper out of the windows. She also has an obsessive interest in "tidying" the toilet paper into the toilet, causing blockage and flooding if flushed. She has unwound toilet rolls and put the paper down the toilet during the day as well as at night. She continues to have self-stimulatory habits such as singing, echolalia, and tapping her nose with cutlery or a finger. Outbursts of more violent self-injury did not stop the moment she crossed the house threshold.

All of these behavioural traits are still present today but they have been changed for the better: lowered in frequency, intensity, or duration. Her sleeping is much more reliable, her self-injury rare, and she no longer throws rubbish out of the window. She continues to put vast amounts of paper down the toilet, which is still problematic but only in terms of the economic and practical consequences! She has been taught which objects it is appropriate to pick up and carry, and where to take them to and put them down; and she no longer wanders round continually clutching some item between her body and her withered left arm. She no longer has long stretches of time to fill with no productive role or responsibility.

In terms of positive skill acquisition, teaching has been part success and part failure. Margaret is able to do many household activities with staff help. She can follow gestural prompts, has some receptive discrimination of spoken language, and has good persistence. Therefore involving her in, say, stacking the dishwasher or emptying, cleaning, and re-stacking the cupboards is easy. Teaching has been needed to give her skills which were not necessary to life in the hospital, for example, how to fill a kettle, how to hang clothes on a hanger, and how to put dirty crockery on the drainer to be washed rather than away in the cupboard. Given the previous absence of toilet tissue she has been taught how to wipe herself and, given the restrictions of life in a long-stay hospital, how to use public conveniences.

Important though such teaching is, and without wishing to diminish the staff achievement and skill in teaching Margaret, who is evidently severely mentally handicapped and has certain autistic characteristics, it is not this kind of skill acquisition from which Margaret's improved quality of life derives. We return to our earlier observation that such programming is the icing on the cake in terms of its significance in Margaret's changed life. The more important change is that Margaret now enjoys the support and direction which enables her to be involved in the stuff of life itself. Indeed, it is much more likely that it is the higher quality of life that promotes developmental growth than that the developmental growth occasions a higher quality existence. Margaret moved from a hospital ward comprising large dormitory, large toilet area, large dayroom, large dining room, and no semblance of private space, to a house with her own bedroom. In her bedroom she has wall-to-wall carpet, a divan bed, wardrobe, dressing table, shelving, and a chest-of-drawers. More importantly, she has a door to close: autonomy to leave and join the society of others.

That sense of autonomy is extended through other aspects of home life of the people living at 10 Summerton Road. It includes the ability of individuals to meet their own basic needs, such as being able to go to the toilet when they choose and to be helped by staff tuition to do so competently; or being able to get a drink of water from the kitchen. It extends to the "more sophisticated" pleasures of life, such as being able to help themselves to a piece of fruit from the fruit bowl. Margaret's new life, like that of her companions has greater responsibility as well as greater autonomy. The house needs cleaning and tidying, crockery and cutlery need washing and drying, clothes need laundering, food needs to be prepared, and the people who live there and generate such requirements, need to meet them. In common with the others Margaret's daily activity has, at the least, such purpose.

Her new life also has a much greater appearance of social order. Margaret lives with six other people with mental handicaps who, with the aid of staff, collaborate with each other. Direct interactions between these individuals do not take up a major part of their day, as most lack the language by which to conduct such social behaviour. But people collaborate, in the sense of contributing to the accomplishment of the household tasks, by doing specific tasks in parallel (such as two people helping to clear the dining room tables, or two people doing the supermarket shopping with a member of staff) and by being considerate of each other (for example, passing a serving dish, condiment, or other item at the meal table, or when making a drink getting one for someone else too). Positive interactions do occur and anti-social exchanges are rare. Also absent are the overpowering impressions of the previous environment in which Margaret lived: depressing noise, and bizarre, psychotic movement. That is not to say that the social milieu of 10 Summerton Road is always perfect: the people who live there do get cross with each other sometimes and respond with physical aggression as their only means of communication. Just as crossing the threshold did not generate instant change in Margaret, the same is also true for other members of the household. People spend time making strange noises and ritualised movements, Margaret included. But the extent and overall balance of impression is utterly different.

Keeping a household running, in the ordinary world at least, requires community contact and involvement in shopping. Respite from the chores of household life often also includes community involvement in the pursuit of leisure activities — going for a drink in a pub, or to activity groups or clubs. It is interesting that it is only when a person has a job, chores, or tasks to do that talking of rest, recreation, and leisure takes on any meaning. Margaret's new life includes such elements. She is often in town, so she needs to look good and she needs to learn how to socialise and how to behave so as to avoid generating adverse reactions. She takes pleasure from being out and about. She has joined a folk club which is held in a room of a local pub. She enjoys evenings there.

Other ways by which people derive purpose in their lives are through work and through the development of intimacy with those to whom they are closest. Margaret does not have a job outside the house, although it is not inconceivable that she could have one. But like most of us she has family. The remainder of this description of Margaret is given to her mother's account of the impact of the move to 10 Summerton Road. It is written in the order that the thoughts came to Mrs. Tarrant. It is as accurate a transcript of her actual words as our notetaking has allowed.

"*The first thing you notice about the hospital — any hospital and the school in fact, well most large places but not here* (10 Summerton Road) — *is the smell. No matter how clean the place is on the surface, there is a smell that tells you that you are among people who are incontinent. It is the first thing you notice; you can't get away from it. But not here, you never get that smell here. Some of the people are incontinent but the staff manage well. It's marvellous really.*

The main difference is that Margaret has come back to her family. I used to visit regularly before; I tried hard but it was too difficult and too far. We used to have Margaret home but no sooner than we got her there, she would want to go back to the hospital. The journey was terrible, Margaret playing up all the time. And then at home she would play up wanting to go back. I didn't know how to stop it or control her. Now she comes to our home and we're in and out of this one. I run into her in Merton. That was a surprise the first time it happened. Just after Margaret had moved here, I saw her walking on the pavement in town with one of the staff. I hadn't expected it, such a normal everyday occurrence. I was driving at the time and I nearly crashed my car. Margaret is now back with the family — I feel it and everyone else at home too, including her sisters; she has a large family, lots of sisters. I used to try to visit her before every week but a visit to hospital is always artificial; it's a special thing a visit. But now she's included in ordinary family activities. It's absolutely wonderful. I feel I am involved in her life again. I did try and the hospital were very good, they tried to let you be involved. I even took washing home. It was no good though because I never saw her wearing the things again, they just disappeared.

Margaret looks better now and her standard of behaviour is much improved. I suppose that they expect so much from her here, she has to get better. I used to be nervous having her with me or at home, she used to play up and I didn't really know what to do. It was so upsetting. I feel better now. She used to scream non-stop and smash things up — she broke two televisions before she went into hospital. In hospital they filled her up with tranquillisers. That can't do anybody any good. Now I can say, "Peggy, sit down a while", and she does. I think she was probably maturing all the time. She went to the hospital as a child and came here as a young adult. But nobody at the hospital told the right story. I would tell them that I would have difficulty with her screaming and they would say that Margaret didn't scream there. But she did, I saw her many times. There was the time she fell and cracked her head and was in the hospital unit just before she came here. They said she had had several fits and fallen. She'd had mild fits before without injury and it's awful but I didn't know whether to believe the consultant. I could never be sure they told me the truth. Then she had another fit here and fell, and I felt terrible for having doubted them.

She had matured at the hospital but she is far more amenable now. She just ignored you before, you couldn't get her to do the things she does now. Margaret has learned to live in the community again. She couldn't learn that at the hospital. Even when they took her out, it was at least twenty in a coach. She was just one in a large group who couldn't be involved.

Margaret went into the hospital when one of her younger sisters was being born. It was just for six weeks. The consultant said that he hoped she wasn't as bad as I had described her because they might not be able to cope. She didn't want to come out. You see, I think that Margaret had to compete with lots of sisters. She knew she was different and didn't want to have to compete. She wanted to go back to the hospital when we brought her home again. She was very upset when we got back home — but, of course, that could have been because we had moved house. That is one way in which she is completely different now since coming here. She will now accept changes in routine, unpredictability. Before she had rituals. You had to do things the same way, go by the same route, go to the same places; she wouldn't go anywhere else. If you changed it would set her off, screaming and tantrumming. At the hospital when I visited, we always went to the café to the same table for a drink. We even had to drive the car the same way. One time when we passed my sister's home instead of calling in, Margaret went mad.

When she was nine, Margaret was said to be autistic. We took the Country Life magazine. Margaret used to collect them, a big pile of them. She liked to open each one at the page with the picture of the society lady and lay them down all over the floor of the living room and up the hall. Margaret would then walk around the magazines looking down at them hitting her chin with her knuckles. It was innocent enough but very strange, hard to explain when visitors came to call, so I tried to stop it. You couldn't tell her not to do it or take the magazines away, she would scream and tantrum. I gradually reduced the pile of magazines without her noticing. She did the same thing thing with the pattern on the carpet, walking round and round looking at it and tapping herself. Then there were the tin lids and mirrors. She got the shaving-type mirrors, the small ones which stand up by themselves, and liked to line them up in front of her when having a meal, watching herself eating. The mirrors used to get broken, swept off the table. I bought practically every mirror they had in Woolworths. I went on to give her tin lids in which to see her reflection instead. She carried them about with her — the noise when she walked!

Margaret carried other things, a rag doll which she had at home and all the time she was at hospital, and still had when she came here. It wasn't really encouraged here, staff said they didn't really like it and thought she should be more adult and more constructively occupied. They got her a handbag to carry. Having younger sisters, when she comes to our home, she has access to dolls. She used to pick those up and carry them around but I would take them from her when it was time to return here and say that they stayed at my house. She can accept things now, I could take them from her without her screaming. The last time she was home, she wasn't even bothered to pick the dolls up to carry round. She carted things about at the hospital all of the time, they couldn't get her to do things instead.

Margaret can now do lots of things she couldn't before. She can make a cup of tea when she comes to our home. She is far more helpful about the house; still very speedy in the way she does things, but helpful. At first, after she had learnt things by being involved here, she wanted to do all the new activities when she came home. She's not so bothered now, but I think that's natural; I have other daughters who have changed like that. But she helps clear up the mess her sisters leave around. I say to them, 'Come on, tidy up, Margaret's coming home and if you don't she'll do it for you'. She helps me put clothes on the line. Her table manners have improved, that is a great thing. She used to eat so fast. They've taught her to slow down in Summerton Road. To do that takes effort every mealtime.

I take Margaret to Mass. All the family go, it is quite possible; marvellous really. She takes Communion. Margaret loves singing and has a lovely voice. If it is a hymn she knows she sings it beautifully. In others, she may sing something rather different. She loves the Christmas carol concert. But if it is a carol that just the choir are to sing, she doesn't sing. She watches me and if I don't sing nor does she.

There is no comparison between her life then and now. One thing I have come to realise is that Margaret is severely mentally handicapped. I'm not sure that I knew before. I just thought of her as wild. At the hospital they learned to control her in some way. She first went to what they called the rumpus room and then to the school. But her social behaviour did not conform to social standards. It does now. I can take her to a café or pub. We do, we go out as a family together. I even went to the theatre one evening and found Margaret sitting in the row in front of me. It was such a surprise. I had never dreamt it possible; they would never have attempted it at the hospital; not as a single person anyway, maybe in a large group with some special dispensation for their behaviour. She was marvellous. She was aware that I was there after about ten minutes but she behaved perfectly all right. The quality of Margaret's life has improved out of all recognition. Anyone would want to lead it as it is now, but no-one would want to be stuck away in the hospital. Although they try hard, it's the system. She has such a full, busy life. One day she was at home with us having lunch and the 'phone went. It was the staff here to ask whether Margaret could come back soon as she was going to the Horse of the Year Show — wonderful, but they did it.

I didn't say this at the time, and I've never told Sandy since, but when it was first suggested that Margaret could come to live here I thought the proposal was a fairy story. I thought, no-one will cope — only one member of staff on duty at night! But then I thought that they only had two at the hospital to thirty-six patients and I realised it was much better here. Margaret was just one of thirty-six patients before — they were patients there, not clients of a service. She just sat, sat all day and rocked. Rocked backwards and forwards, that was her life. There was the odd outing. We took her out. We knew she was bathed specially because we were coming. But she still smelt terribly; you can't get rid of the smell of ages by one short bath. We would drive with the car windows open. I smoked then and would smoke twice as many cigarettes to cover the smell. Her skin is several shades lighter now, being free from the ingrained dirt. Margaret got fat in the hospital. It affected her walking. First she had to have a calliper on her leg and then it was looking like she'd need a wheelchair. She couldn't walk far and needed manhandling to get upstairs. They did realise at the hospital and slimmed her down, but stairs and distances were always a problem. Here she walks up stairs and she can take long walks now. I have to struggle to keep up. Her physical health has improved considerably. The whole atmosphere in the house is better, an atmosphere of a full and busy life. Before she had the existence of a cabbage. I am not saying they didn't try at the hospital but it was pretty hopeless. For example, the way Margaret swallowed food so fast was because if you didn't eat quickly someone else pinched it. I have seen it while being there during teatime. A hand would come over and the food would be gone.

People here are treated with human dignity. You can't get that with open baths and loos, and we all need it don't we? The dormitory in the hospital wasn't entirely open. There were screens to separate the beds. I bought Margaret a bedspread to try and give her a personal corner in the ward. We are a big family and the clothes and presents we took Margaret in the hospital amounted to a lot. Virtually every time anyone visited something would be taken in. But there was nothing left, it was all gone, all disappeared. She came here with just two carrier bags of new clothes, obviously bought for her by the hospital for the occasion because the labels were still on. Nothing we had taken in had survived. Even the gifts from the previous Christmas had gone (Margaret moved in April). *But Margaret herself is tidy. She looks after her things. Everything in her room here is kept just so. She tidies up at home better than her untidy sisters. In hospital she didn't have her own clothes. They just took anybody's. She even had someone else's shoes on once when we visited and she often came out in other people's clothes. I kept taking in good clothes and would get absolutely distraught because she never appeared in them. I kept her coat at home to make sure she had one that was decent when we went out or when she came home. They had clothes sometimes for special occasions, long party frocks, but not the daily necessities. Generally, Margaret would have no bra, or the wrong bra, or the wrong-sized bra. There was open nudity. You could arrive and people might be naked in the doorway, allowed to walk about naked.*

Her elder sisters always understood about her handicap but her younger ones didn't know her. They and her father upset her on visits to the hospital so they didn't go. He's rather gentle and there is a special affection between them, so it was very difficult. Anyway for the younger ones, a visit to the hospital was a nervous ordeal. Now we have a different outlook. They see her at least once a week. Her little sister is really good, very natural in the way she talks to Margaret. They come here and we all go to church together. They can come in here on their own with Margaret. If we are turning the car round, they run on ahead. Her teenage sister is very proud when the girls from the school say they have seen her grown-up sister in town and remark, 'Isn't she pretty?'. Because she is, her appearance has altered totally. She used to have that dreadful long straight hair that she constantly chewed. Look at her now, it's styled. Her clothes are picked just for her, specially to suit her, modern and to fit her. When she was a child at home Margaret always looked good. At the hospital it was impossible, terrible, and now she is here it is good again. The school at the hospital tried to make a stand about people coming presentably dressed. They would refuse to have them in school like that. But they had to give up in the end. They had their own clothes at the school to change people into while they were there.

Margaret now has a community life. I was in Safeways the other day and first I met one of my daughters who is in college in Manchester and had stopped off to do some shopping before coming home, and then I met Margaret. We had a quick chat and then parted. She didn't throw a tantrum, she behaved normally. She is living life like other people. You see when she was in hospital she missed her elder sister's wedding. Had she been here, she could have gone to the wedding and to the reception. She comes home for Christmas Day. That only happened once when she was in hospital; we tried the first time, but not again.

I don't feel this is a hospital. It is just a friendly place, a good atmosphere, everyone's nice to each other. One of the most remarkable things is I never felt it was all programmed. I didn't realise until recently that it's carefully structured. It seems just a friendly, ordinary household — really marvellous."

Elizabeth Shaw: averting death and rebuilding a life

The central issue concerning Elizabeth Shaw's involvement with 10 Summerton Road was literally one of life or death. Elizabeth, a middle-aged woman with Down's syndrome, had been living locally in the family home. Her father had died some time earlier and, out of a large number of children, Elizabeth and two single brothers remained at home; with their now elderly mother looking after them and the household. Some eight years previously, Elizabeth had attended the local authority adult training centre but had refused to continue there following a minor road accident in which her transport was involved on the way to the centre one morning. Following her refusal to attend the day service, Elizabeth had become more or less "lost" to the services as a whole, receiving only occasional, uncoordinated contact. During this time Elizabeth became profoundly withdrawn so that by the time service involvement became more concerted she was in a serious situation.

A year before the opening of 10 Summerton Road Elizabeth's family practitioner, prompted by concern from the social services department to begin to plan Elizabeth's future care, wrote to the consultant psychiatrist at the large mental handicap hospital in the neighbouring health district which still served the Merton area. Mrs. Shaw was approaching her mid-seventies and Elizabeth's brothers and sisters had been frank enough to admit that they were not going to accept the responsibility of caring for Elizabeth should their mother become unable to do so. There was professional concern to avoid a sudden crisis admission to residential care that such an eventuality would cause. The psychiatrist was asked whether periods of short-term care could be arranged to allow mother and daughter to adjust to being apart. Mrs. Shaw was deeply attached to Elizabeth, and devoted to caring for her. She would not hear of Elizabeth leaving home. It seemed that she felt like many parents of people with mental handicaps: believing that only she could adequately care for her child and experiencing such a strong sense of mutual interdependence that she almost wished that the death of her child would coincide with or precede her own demise. Moreover, Elizabeth herself was utterly resistant to any idea of leaving home.

Elizabeth was assessed by the psychiatrist as being in a "psychotic state" and, although short-term places were available, he judged that "an injection of Largactil" would be required to get Elizabeth to leave the house. It would be doubtful, therefore, if such treatment could be judged as being entered into voluntarily. He replied in this way to the family practitioner and the matter was left there. The situation was not known to health district staff involved in planning the new local service at the time. However, in the next two years a number of changes occurred: 10 Summerton Road opened, the family practitioner and the psychiatrist changed, and Elizabeth herself continued to regress and become increasingly withdrawn. There was a delay in the services picking up and responding to Elizabeth's situation; she was on the margin of service awareness.

Some time after 10 Summerton Road opened, and about fifteen months before Elizabeth's eventual admission, the new psychiatrist and the person-in-charge of the house visited Mrs. Shaw to describe the short-term care service of the house and to offer Elizabeth the opportunity to make use of it. Although shy and reticent, Elizabeth was still healthy and, indeed, was slightly plump. Again, service staff were concerned that neither Elizabeth nor the family was in receipt of support and, in view of Mrs. Shaw's age, the home situation was vulnerable. Mrs. Shaw again made it clear that she had no interest in service involvement. Staff felt that Elizabeth was getting little help or support, that she was regressing, and that she was cut off from the outside world. The family practitioner, social worker, and a newly-established community mental handicap nurse were all involved over the next twelve months in trying to arrest a deteriorating situation. Individual programme planning was considered to be the best course to take.

At this time Elizabeth was practically confined to the house. The family as a whole had little social contact and what little Elizabeth had, in the form of a weekly visit with her mother to a neighbour's house, ceased when that neighbour died. Elizabeth had not been into town in eight years. Now it was a matter of whether she could be induced to leave the house at all. Objectives set in the first individual programme planning meeting between the community psychologist, the community mental handicap nurse, the person-in-charge of 10 Summerton Road, Mrs. Shaw, and the social worker — that Elizabeth should accompany her mother to the local newsagents' and the Post Office — were not accomplished. There was no real mechanism for programming such behaviour change. However, at least Elizabeth had been incorporated in some formal system of review and her mother, by attendance, had recognised some form of service involvement.

Rather than becoming more sociable Elizabeth withdrew further, spending most of her time in bed and getting up only to go to the toilet and sometimes to collect the newspaper or letters from the front door mat. This continued over a period of five months. Elizabeth did not even get up for meals and she began consistently to refuse to take food. Her mood became very agitated and changeable. The psychiatrist diagnosed "depression with psychotic overtones" and prescribed 25 mg of Melleril, twice a day. Elizabeth became increasingly thinner and frail, hardly eating or talking. When she did speak it was in a barely audible murmur. The family practitioner tried to be involved and did prescribe her some vitamins, but he had difficulty in gaining access to conduct a thorough physical examination. Elizabeth would not tolerate it, kicking and screaming if approached. Despite considerable effort he managed only to take her pulse.

Elizabeth is intellectually more able than anyone else who has lived at 10 Summerton Road. She has the ability to comprehend what is said to her and to converse when she chooses. Before her illness she could manage most of her own self-care, dressing, grooming, washing, and toileting, needing some help with personal cleanliness in the latter. She was fully ambulant and had unaffected use of all limbs. She underwent such severe regression, however, that she barely did any of these things, and even became incontinent. Her body weight declined to just over four stones, at least two stones below an appropriate weight for her height. Apparently, Elizabeth had lost her adaptive functioning skills and had developed anorexia nervosa; undergoing a sustained and substantial weight loss, associated with refusal to take food. Later medical examination and investigation, accomplished upon admission to residential care, confirmed the absence of any identifiable physical basis for her loss of weight. She ceased to menstruate. As far as is known she did not have other anorexic symptoms, such as disordered feeding patterns, food hoarding, or regurgitation, but her refusal to eat was associated with other behavioural manifestations: profound regression, passivity, social withdrawal, and an agitated state. She also had a distorted sense of her own body image, evidenced by her saying she was "too fat". Certainly, this problem was felt to be sufficiently likely for care staff to avoid making reference to what she looked like in case it was detrimental. Such regression, including anorexic symptoms, is not unknown in the research literature; there is at least one other description of a middle-aged woman with Down's syndrome whose previous adaptive functioning and intellectual ability were much as Elizabeth's.

Whatever diagnostic label should or should not be applied, there was a grave danger that Elizabeth would die. She was very weak and susceptible to illness and the family practitioner had already prescribed courses of antibiotics. Her body weight continued to fall and attempts to coordinate an effective treatment programme within the family home, reliant on Elizabeth's mother as therapist, had not been successful. During this period, the senior staff from 10 Summerton Road had again been involved during the individual programme planning meetings and had arranged for Mrs. Shaw to visit the house so that she could gain a first-hand impression of the service offered. Although she implied no criticism of the house, she had no interest in her daughter using it. She retained the dominant view that she alone could care for Elizabeth, others would not be able to manage, and, of course, Elizabeth was clearly demonstrating a lack of desire to leave her family home. The professionals involved were seriously concerned that Elizabeth was now in grave danger. Her sister had said that Mrs. Shaw did not discuss Elizabeth's care with the family, and she reiterated the family's unwillingness to care for Elizabeth if her mother were unable to continue to do so. The question of whether Elizabeth should be compulsorily admitted for treatment under Section 26 of the *Mental Health Act, 1983* had to be faced.

A special case conference was held in November, 1983. Mrs. Shaw was invited but did not come. Judgement was unanimous that Elizabeth required admission for appropriate treatment but views were divided as to whether urgency dictated compulsory admission then and there, or whether it could be delayed. It was proposed that the family practitioner and community nurse conduct a thorough medical examination and the nurse, social worker, and psychologist visit at least weekly to check the situation of mother and daughter. This demonstration of service determination seemed to have a rapid effect in changing Mrs. Shaw's position, albeit reluctantly, to one of acceptance that Elizabeth should be admitted for treatment to 10 Summerton Road. Within two weeks Elizabeth was admitted, not as a long-term resident, but for treatment only. The overwhelming priority was for the decline in weight to be halted and for Elizabeth to re-establish an appropriate body weight, strength, and level of activity. Another special meeting of the individual programme planning team was held within two months. This was partly to review the residential arrangements but was also prompted by some feeling of dissatisfaction in the way Elizabeth's admission had actually been accomplished.

In the end, events had moved quickly. Admission had taken place less than two weeks after a case conference which had effectively decided against immediate admission but for careful monitoring. There had been no improvement in weight despite her mother's attempts to offer food. The senior social worker, on receipt of the social worker's report, expressed real concern about Elizabeth's physical danger and he again raised the possibility of admission under Section 26. The person-in-charge of 10 Summerton Road was on a week's leave but, on being telephoned at home, had gone into work and then to Mrs. Shaw's house. The psychologist and social worker were upstairs in the bedroom, attempting to encourage and induce Elizabeth to accompany them. Elizabeth was screaming and kicking and doing all in her power to resist. Mrs. Shaw, distraught in the kitchen, was saying, "Why don't you go on then: just take her; go on, take her". On entering this situation, the person-in-charge made a decision. He went upstairs, picked Elizabeth up and carried her, still kicking and screaming, to the car. With the psychologist as escort, he drove Elizabeth to 10 Summerton Road. The social worker stayed with Mrs. Shaw to do what she could to help her.

Elizabeth came to the house late one Friday afternoon. She was moved directly to a bedroom where she spent the remainder of the day. By the next day, staff had managed to get her up and had persuaded her to come down to the living room. This was a welcome success, for the staff shared considerable anxiety and concern that they lacked the skills necessary to care appropriately for Elizabeth. Again the key to their confidence and appropriate performance was careful programming by the senior staff with the aid of a psychologist, a doctor, and a system of detailed recording.

The individual programme plan initially had very basic objectives: to re-establish Elizabeth's intake firstly of fluids and then of food, and the gradual reintroduction of activity. Elizabeth was considerably dehydrated so fluid intake was the first priority. Her fluid and food intake, and whether she was in bed or downstairs, was monitored on a daily form divided into fifteen-minute intervals. The basis of the programme was:

Fluids

Elizabeth should have about three litres of fluid per day. This part of the programme is to encourage her to drink 200mls of fluid every hour, divided into four lots of 50mls, one for every 15 minutes. Each time Elizabeth finishes 50mls, record what the fluid was in the relevant time band on the recording sheet. If Elizabeth has not finished 50mls within an hour make sure she stays or comes downstairs and say to her that she has to drink so much fluid before she can go up to her bedroom. Show her a glass with 100mls and tell her she can go back upstairs after she has finished her drink.

If she takes a mouthful and then dribbles or spits it out, warn her that if she does it again you will put more in her glass. If she does repeat it, refill the glass by approximately the same as the amount wasted. You will need to keep her downstairs until she has drunk 100mls. This often means directing her to sit back in her chair after she has got up. Ignore the following behaviours (they often occur when she is downstairs for a drink or food): crying, slapping, kicking, hair pulling, shouting "no". Reading her a page of a simple story after a mouthful or two helps.

Food
It is also important to encourage Elizabeth to take solids. These should be small amounts at regular intervals, at least two-hourly. Record type of food and amount taken. If food is offered unsuccessfully put X in the relevant hour square. See list of Elizabeth's food preferences.

Activity
Elizabeth should get up for all meals and mid-morning drinks. Try to have her downstairs for one hour in every three, particularly during the day when some of the others are out. Encourage domestic involvement, particularly in the preparation of food.

On her first full day at 10 Summerton Road, Elizabeth drank nearly half a litre of fluid: orange squash and a high-calorie, concentrated glucose drink. She was out of bed and downstairs from 5.00 pm until bedtime at 10.30 pm. She took one taste of the evening meal. On the second day she took a similar amount of fluid, came down for a mid-morning drink, again at lunchtime, and then from 3.30 in the afternoon until she went to bed at 9.45 pm. She increased her intake of the high-calorie drink and took three dessert spoonfuls of oxtail soup. On the third day she walked downstairs herself for the first time, just after 9.00 am. She remained downstairs for the entire day, until 11.30 at night. She chose cornflakes for breakfast and had one spoonful, took a spoonful of beef broth and a bite of banana at lunchtime, seven-and-a-half teaspoonfuls of strawberry yoghurt mid-afternoon followed by a further two at teatime, and three bites of a cheese sandwich during the evening. This progress was maintained. On the fourth day, she ate twelve teaspoonfuls of porridge, ten teaspoonfuls of strawberry yoghurt, seventy ml of beef soup, a square of chocolate, another seventy ml of beef soup, one small bar of chocolate, twelve teaspoonfuls of shepherd's pie, one slice of bread (half Marmite, half jam), and approximately four ounces of fruit cake during a day in which she was up and about from 8.30 am until 11.00 pm.

During Elizabeth's initial period in the house, the general practitioner who attended the household conducted a complete physical examination, including taking blood samples. The examination and subsequent investigations were sufficient to rule out obvious physical causes for the rapid weight loss. Progress in eating continued. Just nine days from the start of the dietary programme, Elizabeth was eating two Weetabix with milk and sugar for breakfast, four ounces of scrambled egg and fried potato and a cheese sandwich for lunch, and a quarter of a quiche lorraine with potato and beans for supper. Her fluid intake had risen to three-quarters of a litre. From the date of admission in mid-November until mid-December, the detailed daily records of food and fluid intake were maintained. By then Elizabeth was beginning to eat better and more consistently and a simpler record of food and fluid intake was adopted and kept until the middle of February.

Elizabeth's weight was monitored daily from the beginning of December until the end of the following July, and thereafter weekly. Her weight increased steadily during the first ten days but less quickly during the next fortnight. By Christmas Elizabeth was four stone twelve pounds (undressed), at least eight pounds heavier than her starting point of four stone four pounds (dressed). Her weight then declined again by four pounds over as many days. During January and February it increased again but fluctuated within the four to five stones range. A dietician's advice was taken in January. Her opinion was that a plateau effect on weight gain at such a stage was to be expected. The only deficiency she thought evident from her investigations was one of insufficient vitamin D, which could be rectified by Elizabeth going out of the house and being exposed to sunlight. From March to July Elizabeth's weight gradually increased to five stone five pounds; since then it has arisen above six stones. Special provision is still being made to ensure that she eats enough food but she now has a pattern of eating mainly at mealtimes like other people in the house. Indeed, the strategy of offering little but often was phased out after good eating was established during the first December. Moreover, staff noticed that Elizabeth usually left something on her plate, however little she was given in the first place, so they began to offer her portions of a size that would be normal for a healthy appetite. The high-calorie glucose drink was only recently stopped but the main reason for its continuation was simply that Elizabeth liked it.

Having described Elizabeth's dietary programme and weight gain up to the present time, we have run on beyond the deliberations concerning the permanency of her stay in the house. The special meeting of the individual programme planning team held in the first December of her stay was attended by all relevant people, except Mrs. Shaw who was invited but did not come. The meeting discussed and recognised Elizabeth's weight gain and the behavioural change achieved during the preceding month but also acknowledged that further improvement was desirable. The social worker had talked to Mrs. Shaw about the need for Elizabeth to spend time away from the family home and reported that Mrs. Shaw was at least considering that Elizabeth might have repeated periodic stays in 10 Summerton Road. She still preferred this idea to the thought of Elizabeth living there permanently, however regular the visits home. But it was also noted that Elizabeth had not expressed a wish to go home or to leave 10 Summerton Road. Nor had she become distressed when her family left after visiting her.

Family members had held back from visiting while Elizabeth settled in. Mrs. Shaw came once in the first fortnight to satisfy herself that Elizabeth was adjusting well and was happy. Other members of the family visited subsequently and Elizabeth now has regular family involvement, a subject to which we will return. The December planning meeting was of the opinion that a long-term place in Summerton Road, with visits home, would be the most suitable arrangement for Elizabeth. With a view to this eventuality, it was decided that a place in the house should be reserved, tentatively, for her use. But it was premature to reach a firm decision until further discussion with Mrs. Shaw had taken place and more time had elapsed in which to gauge Elizabeth's reaction to living away from home. The planning team was also aware of the need to provide support for Mrs. Shaw. She was beginning to go out more than in the past; one week she had been shopping twice and had visited her daughter for coffee. The social worker and community mental handicap nurse agreed to continue to visit her regularly. It was also recognised that Mrs. Shaw had found her visit to 10 Summerton Road stressful and so it was resolved that the person-in-charge should visit her at home to describe Elizabeth's progress and pattern of activity.

As Elizabeth was to stay at 10 Summerton Road, in the short-term at least, and as the immediate concern over her health and weight was receding, the area of programming and focus for change began to be expanded. Elizabeth had been admitted in a state of behavioural regression. She was doubly incontinent, having no control over her bowels and dribbling urine. She had lost self-care behaviours such as taking herself to the toilet. She tended to dribble at the mouth and wiping her mouth continuously was causing soreness. Her skin was dry and in poor condition. She had bad haemorrhoids. This, linked with a problem of constipation, meant that she was taking three different laxatives which probably did not assist her to remain continent.

Treatment of the haemorrhoids was started on admission and reinstatement of urinary continence was emphasised early on as part of the whole issue of Elizabeth being up and about more. By the December meeting, Elizabeth was reliably taking herself to the upstairs toilet from her bedroom and before bathing, but was more reluctant when downstairs. This was still leading to occasional incontinence which was one of the targets for continued change. A list of Elizabeth's preferred activities about the house had been drawn up and she was being encouraged to join in doing them as often as she liked. In early December, Elizabeth had been into the garden for a short time and had seemed to enjoy it. It was decided to encourage her to walk around the garden more and then to venture out as far as the local shops. It was also decided that she should work towards going home for a visit. If she did prove to be genuinely phobic about travelling by car, a programme would need to be designed. (A phobic reaction had been cited as the reason why Elizabeth had refused to go to the adult training centre following the slight accident in which she had been involved. That occasion had been the last time she had travelled in any form of transport before being taken from her home to 10 Summerton Road.)

Another conscious aspect of programming, once the immediate concern about weight loss had been remedied, was to give Elizabeth a positive view of herself. If Elizabeth had some form of self-image, the aim was to enhance it; changing her view of herself as a dependant, helpless child to that of a responsible adult. At a very obvious level, she had few clothes that fitted her after losing so much weight. New clothes bought or provided by the family were adult in style. Her hair was styled and attention was given to her appearance, with the intention that she should feel attractive. At the same time it was felt she should assume a greater responsibility for the household tasks her life generated. From December she, like everyone else living in the house, started to be involved in the systems operated for planning activity generally and for acquiring specific teaching goals. A programme for staff, setting out how and when to respond to Elizabeth when she cried, was formalised. This included an emphasis on how to prevent Elizabeth using crying as a means of avoiding making a contribution to household life. At another level, the dryness in her skin referred to earlier was treated by adding baby oil to her bath water.

Elizabeth grew into living permanently at 10 Summerton Road. The individual programme planning meeting, held at its routine time three months after the special meeting called to review her admission, recognised the general change in the family view which had now fallen in line with the professional judgement expressed at the special meeting. Once the permanence of her stay was settled, her family began to take an active interest and staff began to meet members of Elizabeth's extensive family network. Many family members have brought her clothes; as a consequence she has a large wardrobe. Elizabeth goes to her mother's home every weekend, for tea one weekend and to stay overnight on alternate weekends. One of her brothers who still lives at home walks to 10 Summerton Road to collect her and they walk back together. A married sister living in Merton also sees Elizabeth regularly, about twice a week. She and Mrs. Shaw have attended all the individual programme planning meetings about Elizabeth since the two special meetings which discussed and reviewed her admission. They have come to accept and support the service involvement and they now both contribute to the content of the service programme.

Elizabeth's visits home started after she had been on her first successful shopping trip from 10 Summerton Road. That had taken place at the end of January, two months after coming to live at the house. A good deal of persuasion had been needed to get

Elizabeth to venture outside the house, but once out she had enjoyed herself. She had gone to the shops and had a drink in the café. She had even met her brother while out quite coincidentally (again indicating some of the advantages of a local service). It was a great occasion for them both; the first time Elizabeth had been in her local town centre for eight years. This outing was quickly followed by an appointment at the hairdresser's and a visit to a pub. Elizabeth even started to initiate outings. She still does not go out as frequently as some others in the house, but she now chooses whether to go out or not. Going out is not a problem. Elizabeth probably averages about two outings a week, other than those involving visiting relatives.

In the last year, Elizabeth has re-established her self-help skills and is participating more and more in domestic life and household shopping. She is a little more sociable and outgoing than before, though still shy and reticent. She has travelled in cars again. She is fully continent and basically fit and healthy. She has a good relationship with members of her immediate family who are supportive of the service and have a good relationship with service staff. Elizabeth's world is expanding again; she is provided with a service that is programming new experiences for her, is teaching her new skills, and is making sure that the simple, obvious things she needs are done (such as getting her eyesight tested). Establishing an alternative means of occupation during the working day is also part of the agenda — possibly re-attendance at the adult training centre, possibly outside employment. Elizabeth's attendance at review meetings as a member of her own individual programme planning team is also something for the not-too-distant future.

Kathleen Wright: leaving home but staying close

Once sufficient community services become available to provide appropriate and adequate coverage, people with mental handicaps who require residential care will be able to move from their family home to an alternative residence locally. This will avoid the dislocation of ties with friends, family, and locality which still characterises most mental handicap services to this day. The small home service at 10 Summerton Road serves a sector of Merton and its surrounding countryside which has been worked out to provide a match between the number of places provided and the demand for residential care. It is designed to serve its catchment area comprehensively in terms of provision of intensively-staffed, residential accommodation for adults who are more severely and profoundly mentally handicapped. Now that the initial relocation of residents from distant institutions with kinship ties to the territory has been achieved, it is intended that in future the people admitted will have been resident locally in family households. The only exception to this policy is, as in the case of Margaret Tarrant, when the next-of-kin of an institutional resident moves to live within the catchment area. Thus, even though the initial emphasis of the community-based alternative service is in part deinstitutionalisation, once that is achieved the function of the service becomes almost entirely one of serving local community citizens, much in the same way as a school serves local children. The role of the service in relation to Kathleen Wright illustrates this.

During the first two years that 10 Summerton Road was open, Kath lived at home with her mother and father and then, following the death of her father, with her mother alone. Her parents were both retired and Kath herself was in her mid-forties. Her three brothers and her sister had all left home, although one brother returned to stay at weekends. Kath herself attended the local adult training centre five days a week. Apart from this, and an evening at the local Gateway Club once a fortnight, she had little occupation outside the home.

Kath is a shy, anxious person, who is without physical handicap or any obvious physical signs of mental handicap. She does, however, look older than her years and has a hunched-up posture and tentative movements. She is reticent, usually talking only when spoken to. She often withdraws from the activity of the adult training centre, preferring to stand alone near the workshop door. She also often cries for no apparent reason, either when alone or when answering apparently innocuous questions. She talks in sentences with appropriate grammatical structure, but her conversation shows little evidence of mature reasoning and is stylised and repetitive. She talks of herself as a child and in defensive vein, perhaps in imitation of what others have said about her: "I'm not a naughty girl, am I?"; "I'm not that handicapped, am I?". Thus, though her language may have some developed content it serves no developed, positive function. It does not, for example, seem to provide her with a means of controlling her environment by making demands of others around her, or to help her gain an understanding of the world. Although her spoken language has elements of sophistication, Kath is poor at following instructions and is as slow to learn as the other people we have described in this book. She needs a great deal of encouragement to do simple everyday things, let alone attempt to do anything new. She sometimes becomes very agitated when demands are made of her. Her anxiety, and even her speech, may serve a defensive function to deflect such demands. As a result her adaptive and intellectual skills appear underdeveloped. She is more handicapped than she seems; probably less able than she might have been had her abilities and confidence been nurtured and stretched.

In describing Kath's involvement with the service we would like to highlight three of its aspects which appear particularly relevant for her: the nearness of the residential service to her family home which enabled Kath to maintain other important parts of her life undisrupted; the development of adulthood in her personal appearance and in her role as a responsible contributing member of the household; and, the development of her confidence, assertiveness, and an improved self-perception.

Local proximity

Local residential services allow people who are likely to be future service users to come into contact with them before they actually need them. When the time comes for them to require full-time residence they also allow people to keep their existing personal and service ties intact after admission. Before moving to live at 10 Summerton Road on a permanent basis Kath had received periodic, regular, short-term stays. As a result of these stays she had got to know Carol quite well. When Carol obtained a place in the adult training centre which Kath attended the care staff set out deliberately to foster shared interests between them. Carol was interested in going to the cinema, concerts, and for evenings out generally. Kath had a fairly restricted social life. Therefore, long before Kath became a permanent member of the household, Carol and a member of staff would occasionally call for her and they would go out together. Carol and Kath now share a room together.

Living locally means that other relationships have been

maintained. Although the time Kath spends with her mother has declined since she has left home, they still see a lot of each other but the character of such contact has changed. A change has also occurred in Kath's relationship with her brother, sister-in-law, and two nieces. Kath stays with her mother for one weekend every fortnight. By doing so she keeps in contact with one of her brothers who also comes to stay at weekends. She sees her other brother and his family, who live locally, every week as Kath and her mother are both invited to dine with them on Wednesday evenings. This level of family involvement, together with the evenings out that Kath has with Carol and other people from the house, means that Kath has a very full social life. Out of personal choice she has continued going to the Gateway Club, held every other Monday evening; another example of existing ties and relationships being maintained by virtue of the local nature of the residential service. In addition, Kath has retained her place at the local adult training centre during the day and the ties she has there. The length of time one may be on the waiting list for such a facility has been well illustrated in the accounts of the people who have returned to the locality from distant institutions. The situation is analogous for someone who has to move out of the area served by a day-care service that is already being provided in order to receive a residential service.

Unfortunately Mrs. Wright was presented with a less than free decision concerning her choice about whether Kath should continue to live at home with her or should move to 10 Summerton Road. From its inception, 10 Summerton Road had offered a short-term care service. This was generally not frequently used but had been taken up on a regular basis by one or two families, including Kath's. Kath began by having one week-end stay per month. Her family wanted her to live at the house permanently when the time came, but did not want it to be yet. The service agreed to keep them informed on the occupancy of the house. Before his death, Kath's father expressed a wish for her to continue to live in the family home. Mrs. Wright wanted to fulfil this wish, but at the same time she wanted Kath to stay at 10 Summerton Road more regularly. Kath began to stay from Friday to Tuesday alternate weeks. Shortly afterwards, as part of the council's improvement programme to the housing stock, Mrs. Wright was temporarily rehoused and arrangements were made for Kath to stay full-time in Summerton Road during this period.

However, pressure for a decision on admission now came from the health authority's finance department.

10 Summerton Road had never been conceived of as part of a deinstitutionalisation programme, but as a means of providing a community service. On the rationale that it could not be expected that the intentions of people with severe and profound mental handicaps and their relatives, in demanding use of a residential service, would fall conveniently in line with an authority's decision to provide one, it was envisaged that full occupancy of the house would take a matter of some months or years to achieve. Such a rationale was stronger among those providing the service, who were closest to the needs of service users and their families, than among the treasurers of the authority, but a certain tolerance of under-occupancy was created over the first two years. The house had been approaching full occupancy when Richard and Mary had unexpectedly died. Although the extent of occupancy does not affect the total revenue expenditure, it does inflate the revenue costs per person to a level which begins to be described as excessive. Moreover, the auditors wondered why the authority was proposing to provide further facilities elsewhere while existing services had "spare capacity". Mrs. Wright was told of the pressures coming from the bureaucratic centre to move to full occupancy and was warned that if she wanted to ensure Kath had a place she should accept it while it was available. After consideration, this is what she chose to do, although her decision can hardly be represented as a free and unconstrained choice.

Having made the adjustment to Kath living at 10 Summerton Road, Mrs. Wright is very supportive of the service. She regularly attends the individual programme planning meetings for her daughter and has expressed a desire to become more involved in the house generally and in the lives of the other people living in it. For example, she has suggested that Carol might come with Kath to stay at the week-end and she gave Carol a present for her last birthday. Thus, from the viewpoint of both Kath and her mother, the establishment of this local service can be seen to protect people's ties to the past, recognise their current interests, and set the foundations for new networks of relationships to grow in the future. Perhaps one of the most graphic illustrations of how having a local service can allow people with mental handicaps to keep important personal ties is that Kath can still visit and lay flowers on her father's grave.

Assumption of adulthood and the development of confidence and self-esteem

When we first knew Kath, we saw her as someone who was very shy and nervous, like a submissive child who would reply when spoken to but would otherwise sit or stand apart from the mainstream of activity around her. After living at 10 Summerton Road for a little under two years she retains these essential characteristics, but to a lesser degree. Certainly one conscious line of effort has been to bring Kath out of herself, to shift her own, and her family's, perception away from one of her as a child, to increase her participation in life around her, and to encourage her to make choices and yet be more carefree.

The relatively easy part of achieving such a prescription concerns the more obvious symbols of adulthood and status: her appearance, and the way she is approached and talked to by other people. In her mid-forties, Kath physically looked older than her years, but other aspects of her appearance were child-like such as having flat-heeled shoes and long, straight hair gathered at the back. Her mother was not at first amenable to Kath having her hair cut and styled but was eventually convinced by the argument that her hairstyle was difficult for Kath to manage herself. It took considerable staff time to comb it every day and prevent it tangling, just as it had taken similar amounts of her mother's time previously. With a mature, well-groomed hairstyle, smart high-heeled shoes, and new clothing in the style of a smart, middle-aged woman, Kath is less easy to treat as a child. She can read a few words (a small social-sight vocabulary) and she now has a pair of reading glasses. A hearing loss, not previously identified, means that she now has a hearing aid. In themselves, such devices are not particularly exceptional. However, not having them contributes further to a person's functional handicap. If correctly chosen the type and style of spectacles or aid can be strongly symbolic of age and status.

The way people who are not handicapped talk to those who are is amenable to change. It does not involve changing the behaviour of the person who is handicapped but that of other people in contact with that person. It is part of the ethos of the house that everyone who lives there is treated politely. This involves treating people in an adult way, viewing them as being capable of making informed choices, and with reciprocity or equality in social dealings. For example, if staff want people living in the house to come with them when they want them to do something, then those people ought to have the same ability to get staff to accompany them when required. If staff wish members of the household to look on them as friends, and be on first name terms with them, then first name terms should be reciprocated. In addition, examples of friendship can be offered by staff outside of work. When first coming to live at the house, Kath was submissive and juvenile in her dealings with most adults. In her family she was treated as a child, to the extent that even her young nieces (eight to ten years old) were explicitly given a supervisory role in relation to her. Outside her family, she dealt with adults as a school child would; she called everyone "Sir" or "Miss" according to their sex. She defended herself against criticism or demand by weeping. This characterised, and to a large extent still characterises, her behaviour at the adult training centre. In the house, however, staff have consistently encouraged her to use Christian names and to make demands. If she wants something, she is encouraged to ask for it; to express her wants, such as a simple desire for a cup of tea. If she wants social attention she is encouraged to approach others in order to gain it, rather than sitting or standing in a weepy or agitated state until someone asks, "What's wrong?".

Some success has been achieved in changing Kath's behaviour. Crying has declined. She will sometimes ask for things; and she is beginning to make simple choices and express preferences, such as between different breakfast cereals. She has been brought more into the household activity, as an equal participant, pulling her weight. She has learned to do many domestic activities which she had no opportunity to do before. Since she has practised tham at 10 Summerton Road she is able to do them in the family home when visiting her mother; an example not only of the generalisation of learning from one situation to another but of the changed family perceptions of Kath. Family members have responded partly to the example set by staff in the house, partly to Kath's changed appearance and behaviour, and partly because of the progress they have seen in other people living at Summerton Road. They now treat Kath in a much more grown-up way. Kath's sister-in-law recently worked as a volunteer, escorting Shirley to and from work. She was struck by the incongruity of her inclination to hold Shirley's arm or hand — Shirley being mentally handicapped, deaf, and partially sighted — while escorting her along the pavement, knowing that she has mastered a job of paid work. She realised that there were obvious parallels to be drawn in thinking about how to treat Kath.

The fact that Kath has left home has generated for her family the feeling that she is now an independent person, much more effectively than would ever have been achieved by our simply having taught her independence skills. Kath's family now talk about her as an independent person. Her nieces are now less frequently in the situation of looking after Kath and they talk to her much more as an aunt these days.

Socially, Kath likes many things, but as a spectator rather than as a participant. She likes and goes regularly to the cinema, pubs, a local folk club, and concerts, as well as to watch events at the sports centre. As she grows in confidence and independence there is no reason why the horizons of her life should not continue to expand.

CHAPTER 7

Linda Chandler — some successes, some failures

In telling the story of 10 Summerton Road and of the nine people who have lived there we have, with one exception, sequenced the accounts in the order in which the people came to live in the house. We have now come to our last account, that of Linda, the exception to the chronological order. We have chosen to tell her story last partly to finish with a full chapter devoted to a single account, but partly to emphasise one issue in Linda's story; namely, that her admission to 10 Summerton Road was not clear cut. It is difficult to state a precise date as to when it occurred. There was an extended period of indecision in her initial experience of the service during which she lived mostly at home but also sufficiently in 10 Summerton Road for her to be viewed officially as someone living there permanently. Linda became involved with the service on opening but did not come to spend most of her week there until fifteen months later, after Richard and just before Margaret had moved in. A more decisive course might have been to Linda's benefit. Indeed a feeling of dissatisfaction with our efforts on behalf of Linda runs throughout her story. There has been some achievement, but it has been reached with considerable difficulty. Progress has been slower and decision-making more problematic than for some of the other people we have discussed.

First involvement

Linda lived locally and attended the special care unit of the local authority adult training centre. She lived with her parents and elder sister. Her sister was a member of the parent group which met the people planning the 10 Summerton Road service monthly prior to its opening. We have already referred to the differences of opinion that arose concerning the admission policy for the house. Members of the parent group were keen to have a panel judging the priority of individual need upon which they would have representation. We argued for a service on demand, and held to the view that it was not possible to weigh one person's need against another's. In the short-term, while service supply was still deficient, some people would necessarily have to wait. The nub of the argument lay in the fact that, as we have described, Catherine's family were in desperate need and the local parents' group was looking for an arrangement which would guarantee Catherine an immediate service. We also had the impression that they considered a residential place for Linda as another immediate priority.

Linda was eligible for admission to the house within the policy stated by the authority. The availability of a place was made clear to her parents and sister in the round of domiciliary visits which were conducted in preparation for its opening. Linda's parents, however, were not pressing for her to leave home immediately. They could see that she would require a residential service in the future and appreciated that one would be available but they were content for her to continue to live at home for the time being.

Linda's family had developed better cooperation from Linda than staff could manage, either in her day-care setting or later in the house. At various times they have registered surprise when it has been reported to them that Linda has been presenting problems to the services dealing with her. Linda behaved differently at home; her difficult behaviours were least in evidence there.

Over many years, both as a child and as an adult, Linda has posed major problems of management to the education, social services, and health services that she has attended. She has been frustrating to work with because she has given a hint of hidden abilities which she would not subsequently display, masking them by a dominant overlay of repetitive, bizarre, self-stimulatory behaviours and a stubborn, non-compliant attitude which paid no regard to the efforts of staff on her behalf.

Linda has Down's syndrome, is short in stature (less than five feet tall) and, when first in contact with us, was very overweight. Her face, around her mouth and eyes, was sore and inflamed. She had straight hair, simply cut. Her mother said she liked to keep her looking young. She put considerable effort into the clothing she bought and adapted for her. She would buy dresses which were sufficiently broad for Linda to get into and then alter their length so that the hem came just above her knee. When sitting or walking her dresses tended to ride up, revealing her thighs and the top of her tights. She often needed to pull her dress off her bottom entirely when sitting in order to be comfortable.

The main problem was one of cooperation. Although affectionate to staff, Linda tended not to follow their requests. She would reinforce her decision not to join in by deliberately being destructive, deliberately wetting herself, or by being aggressive (pinching, punching, and pulling hair). Staff could have been forgiven for thinking she was baiting them; for example, by pouring a half-full cup of coffee down the front of her dress while they were watching. In the time she thereby created to be left by herself, Linda engaged in a variety of self-stimulatory arm movements, finger movements, head movements, facial grimacing, and vocalisations, sometimes singly but most often in complex combinations.

Beginning to shape the residential care programme

Discussion with Linda's family resulted in Linda embarking on a gradual transition from living at home to living in the house. At the beginning of 1982, Linda began to stay at 10 Summerton Road at week-ends with a view to moving in permanently over the next three months. But the three month period extended to fifteen months. During that time, Linda's sister had three long working trips to the United States. While she was away, the decision to change from Linda staying only at week-ends to living more permanently at 10 Summerton Road could not be reached. Linda's parents said that such a change must wait for her return. Service involvement in relation to Linda, and Linda's own state of residence, was therefore held in limbo for the rest of the year. Linda was a week-end guest but she lived mostly in her family home; her greatest service involvement being still with the special care unit. As a consequence the first fifteen months was a time during which certain directions for movement were identified but little was achieved. Overall, our impression of "phased-care", which we experienced with both Linda and Kath, is that it was of little benefit to either person. It generated confusion rather than adjustment.

Other than the programme planning issues surrounding Linda's admission to long-term care itself, objectives set at this time concerned her appearance and her repertoire of problem behaviours. Linda's strong tendency towards not following instructions competed with the likelihood of her becoming involved in meaningful occupation, interfered with her ability to learn, and caused her to be denied opportunities for participation in community settings. Teaching objectives concentrated on self-help and household skills; establishing full continence was another early concern.

Improvement of Linda's appearance included three elements: weight reduction, through diet such as was in progress with Catherine; treatment of the discolouration of her skin arising from the soreness around her mouth and eyes; and, the encouragement of a more adult wardrobe, footwear, and hairstyle. The first two of these objectives were clearly relevant to her immediate and longer term comfort and health. Added to these, Linda's self-stimulatory rituals and mannerisms had a profound effect on her appearance. Even if her size were to be reduced drastically and her style of dress brought into line with that associated with a woman in her middle-to-late thirties, Linda would remain conspicuously peculiar by virtue of her chosen activity.

Reviewing these objectives with the benefit of hindsight, it becomes clear how unhelpful the extended period of "phased-care" was to beginning the process of change, let alone to gaining its successful achievement. While Linda continued to live mainly with her parents it was natural that the bulk of her wardrobe should be kept at their house. Her weight was largely determined by the diet she followed at home and at mid-day at the day service. Moreover, there was constant interruption to the development of a strategy by which gradually to increase her cooperation and involvement in household life. It was difficult to develop a consistent approach to dealing with Linda's non-compliance, let alone her array of stereotypic behaviour. Through the first two review meetings, objectives were largely recorded as unattained, still in progress, or not even programmed. Apart from supporting a general introduction to the full range of household activities available to her in the course of her regular stays, the residential service could not generate behavioural development in two days a week. The residential staff made a contribution to the discussion and content of the individual programme planning but this in itself had little effect, other than in setting a foundation for the future.

Spending more time at the house: the service begins to respond to Linda's difficult behaviour

Throughout 1982, Linda's needs as we perceived them remained largely unmet. This was during the period in which substantial progress was being achieved for Shirley, Catherine, and Mary. By comparison, there was a feeling among those concerned with the house that the service had failed Linda. We could not help thinking that we might be avoiding the difficult issues that had to be faced in developing a service intervention that would be in her best interests.

In January 1983, Linda changed from living at 10 Summerton Road at weekends to living there during the week but going to visit her family at weekends. This meant that she spent four nights per week in the house but because she also attended a day service Monday to Friday she was still there very much on a part-time basis. When in the house she had a disrupting influence and staff were keen to become more effective in helping Linda settle and enjoy life more. Their concern for the continuing damage that Linda's behaviour was causing to the management of the household, to the way other people viewed her, to the growth of genuine affection towards her, and to her own progress and development was shared by the staff of the special needs unit of the training centre. They had, after all, been looking after Linda longer and as well as seeing her disturbed, non-compliant behaviour as an obstacle to her own development were feeling personally worn down by the task of competing against it and putting up with it. No-one had an immediate strategy as to what to do about the problems Linda presented.

At this point, it may be helpful to give both a definition of the term "self-stimulatory behaviour" and a fuller description of how Linda behaved. "Self-stimulatory behaviour" is a term given to a group of different body, limb, or finger movements and to the making of noises which appear to the outside observer to serve no meaningful or comprehensible adaptive purpose. These events are also called "stereotyped" behaviours: each person's self-stimulatory behaviours being repetitively the same and following ritualistic patterns. Common and obvious examples of such behaviours are body-rocking (repetitive bending at the waist to cause deflection from and return to a vertical position, either when sitting or standing), pacing (back and forth or in a circle), and repetitive hand movements in front of the eyes. Other forms include repetition of noises, repeating words (echolalia), and visual fixation to a light source or some form of motion (often circular). The term "self-stimulation" is based on an inference that, in the absence of an identifiable external consequence to the behaviour, the person must derive pleasurable internal stimulation through activation of the central nervous system.

Linda performed many of these behaviours including body rocking, arm movements, flicking of her fingers, making the noise "amp" repetitively, shaking her head, pulling faces, and violently throwing her head back. Whereas most people have funny little mannerisms that become insignificant and even unnoticed in their constant stream of varied, constructive activity, a few develop such behaviours as their dominant form of occupation, to the exclusion of virtually everything else. The behaviours then constitute a serious problem, appearing to block alternative sources of sensory input. They become highly treasured forms of activity that may be defended by temper tantrums, destructiveness, aggression to others, or self-injury. They interfere with social processes, with the development of meaningful relationships, and with learning from others. They also affect other people, particularly if they do not understand the nature of the problem. Self-stimulatory behaviours can be intrusive and wearing; people can get annoyed and frustrated if the person displaying them cannot be stopped from behaving in such a way. In a group situation the person in question may have no interest in the group activity; the disruption caused may detract staff attention and disturb the attention and enjoyment of others. All these factors are likely to result in the person becoming vulnerable to being excluded from many situations which contain opportunities for meaningful occupation. Even though the person may voluntarily avoid making good use of such opportunities, loss of opportunity may still be considered an important negative consequence. It is important, when staff develop competency to care effectively for such a person, that the person should still be allowed to remain in a situation where there are opportunities that can be exploited to the person's advantage.

Although Linda had begun to live at 10 Summerton Road more than previously, she still went home regularly at weekends. She also spent a number of complete weeks with her family during holiday times. At the March 1983 individual programme planning meeting, the subject of her inappropriate behaviour was again raised by staff from both the house and the special needs unit. It was agreed that some attempt to analyse her behaviour should be made. An American expert in behaviour modification was working with us at that time and he was asked to make an assessment in liaison with the staff of the services concerned and the community psychologist. Linda's behaviour was carefully observed: during lunch-time breaks at the adult training centre; in the special needs unit both while Linda was involved in activity and while she was left alone; and, later in the day, on returning to the house. The observations looked for any pattern in the onset, duration, and cessation of repetitive noises or movements which could be linked to environmental events: specifically, whether staff were contacting Linda, whether staff were leaving her alone, whether demands were being made of her, whether she was free to choose her activity, whether she was alone or with other people, and whether staff were giving attention to other people.

The assessment yielded a number of conclusions. First, Linda engaged in some form of self-stimulatory movement or vocalisation virtually all of the time. There were differences in intensity or modulation which appeared to be related to the attention and demands she was given, but there were seldom times when she was not engaging in some form of stereotypic behaviour. Second, this observation held true over a number of environmental conditions and staff behaviours. This suggested that her behaviour was not closely linked to what was going on around her. Third, while the amplitude of Linda's stereotypic behaviours (including visible signs of emotional upset and associated non-compliance) may serve to deflect staff demands to become involved in alternative activity, staff in the special needs unit and at the house met with some success in asking Linda to do things. Certain approaches were more successful than others. Nonetheless, such behaviours continued as a constant backdrop to other activity.

Although, following assessment, no specific recommendations were made to reduce Linda's self-stimulatory behaviours the following procedure for staff interaction was recommended as a means of gaining her cooperation:

1. *Give clear, short instructions to Linda in a calm tone of voice, soft to medium volume.* (This was noticed to be particularly effective when the staff member's face was very close to Linda's while the instruction was being given. If necessary the staff member was to touch her on the side of the face to gain her attention.)

2. *If Linda does not follow the instruction, repeat it in the same words, tone, and volume of choice.* (If the initial

instruction had been given from some distance across the room, the member of staff was to move closer and repeat the instruction face to face with Linda.)

3. *If Linda still does not follow the instruction repeat it, this time with a physical prompt.* (Examples of the kind of physical prompt required are: if Linda is to pick up a dropped tissue, the staff member should take her hand and move it about twelve inches in a downward direction and then let go; or, if she has to pick up a jug from the table the staff member should push her hand some three inches towards it.)
4. *If Linda does not respond by this stage, physically guide her entirely through what is needed.* (From our observations Linda is unlikely not to have responded to the procedure followed in 3.)
5. *After she has finished, thank her.* (Linda had showed distress on some occasions when immediately asked to do exactly the same thing again. Staff were to avoid directly repetitious activities and to try to think of how to structure activities so that Linda would have a chance to do several different things before being asked to repeat the first response again. Alternatively, they could consider allowing some time to elapse before asking her to repeat the required action again.)

In relation to Linda's repertoire of self-stimulation, our American colleague was not optimistic that a modification strategy based only on positive reinforcement would prove effective. He saw little hope of successful suppression through the systematic deployment of attention to other behaviours or other positive educative means. He thought we would have to consider direct, active, and consistent discouragement of her behaviour.

We could appreciate the truth behind this advice without necessarily welcoming it. There is a general ethos in favour of employing positive means to change behaviour, ones that are educative in nature and are used generally and widely within a person's social culture. There are ethical concerns when aversive means of control are employed, which must be properly addressed. The intention is to find an acceptable means to reach a desirable end. In so doing it is important not to shirk the responsibility to help someone in need of treatment, even if the means are difficult. The end result may be important enough to merit the approach chosen but it is easy to predict that the mere discussion of the possible use of punitive strategies will almost certainly occasion hostile reactions from others. People may not always share the same aspirations for people with mental handicaps in general, or for a particular individual. They may not agree on the definition of benefit or on the suggested course of action to be taken.

Introducing aversive measures is not an easy matter. It is, in fact, far easier to leave the pool unrippled; to live with the *status quo*, knowing that there will be no tangible consequence for failing to address the issue, other than the pricking of one's conscience in knowingly avoiding action on a dependent person's behalf. Neither the house staff nor the day-care staff would be unusual in declaring themselves unable to bring about a dramatic change in Linda's behaviour. Nobody else was stating the need for it to be changed. Nobody else was looking for improvement in the quality of Linda's life, her abilities, her experience of life, or what she got out of it. Her parents seemed content with circumstances as they were and Linda had no other advocate, outside of the services, acting on her behalf. Linda herself, although seemingly deriving little pleasure from her daily round, had never stated any desire for change. (She appears to have greater language ability than she uses, it being masked by her self-stimulatory behaviours. It is difficult to assess her ability accurately but, in her most lucid moments, it is possible to have a meaningful conversation with her based on the exchange of phrases. On the *Derbyshire Language Scheme* (Knowles and Masidlover, 1982) rapid assessment, Linda can hold and respond to three information carrying words: verb, preposition, object. However, there is a danger of overgeneralising the impression of her ability. The fact that she can sometimes converse in short sentences does not mean that she always could if she so chose.)

If programmes of management involving punishment are to be entered into, they must be established in a proper manner, following full consultation and with a proper consideration of the importance for the individual of the target behaviour change. An estimate must be made of what would result from successful programme implementation, and how this would compare to the person's future circumstances if the problem behaviours were to continue unaffected. It is desirable to examine alternative positive strategies directly, rather than relying on expert opinion that they might prove fruitless. It is important to consider whether full suppression of the undesirable behaviour is desirable or practical. For example, in relation to self-stimulation, it might be decided to retain certain times and places where the person can choose to continue to behave in such a way, for example, while having a break from household chores in the living room. Before embarking on any routine strategy of management throughout the day, it is necessary to make sure that the procedure to be adopted is effective and that staff are willing and competent to implement it.

A further difficulty in interpretation and decision-making as far as Linda was concerned, was the report of her behaviour at home. The extent of her inappropriate behaviour was viewed as being much lower by her family than by service staff. In interviewing Mrs. Chandler for research purposes, she reported that Linda did not threaten or inflict injury on other people, and that she did not damage property or have temper tantrums. She also said that Linda did not disrupt others' activities or display a lack of consideration of others, except for occasionally disturbing people watching television in order to gain their attention. The only stereotyped mannerisms she reported were body rocking and rubbing hands together. She made no mention of any peculiar noises or repetitive vocalisations. She did say that Linda was occasionally upset when thwarted or criticised, and that she was overly particular about where and how to sit; liking to sit with both legs crossed on the chair. In a similar interview with residential care staff, Linda was reported to show a more extensive variety of self-stimulatory behaviours and more serious problems of aggression to people and property.

The difference between accounts of Linda's behaviour in the family and at 10 Summerton Road did not seem to be one of different perceptions of the same behaviour. It was clear that Linda behaved differently; even if the difference was less extreme than the impression given by the two conflicting reports. Why? She may have been happier at home. Other factors may also have been relevant. Few demands were made of her at home and her chosen pursuits seemed to be accepted more. Requests for her to change what she was doing were likely to be fewer. We had seen, in our observations of Linda, that in a situation which presented few demands or responsibilities and providing she was allowed to sit as she pleased, Linda's self-stimulatory behaviours were considerably muted. We had also seen the amplitude and intensity of her self-stimulatory behaviours increase to overcome demands made of her, escalating to shouting accompanied by visible signs of distress. An absence of demands might explain why her family did not report examples of aggressive behaviour towards them or the deliberate spoiling of household property. The home environment was tolerant and accepting, and Linda was secure in the love of her family.

While we were still pondering the interpretation and implications of the analysis of Linda's behaviour, circumstances changed within 10 Summerton Road which became of more immediate concern. Linda had always received considerable staff attention, second only in extent to Catherine. Despite staff efforts to help her settle and to be an integral part of household life, Linda began to react by displaying a range of "house-wrecking" behaviours. In damaging the environment she affected others living in the house and hurt the feelings of some staff, causing them anguish. Staff had to attend to the consequences of her behaviour, thus reducing further the amount of time they had available to spend positively with her and the other members of the household.

Linda's disruptive behaviours fell into four categories. Although not all of them were strictly new, there was a marked increase in the severity and frequency of their occurrence. One category concerned damaging the house or making an unjustifiable mess: breaking crockery, tipping over drinks or plates of food, knocking objects such as plant pots or ornaments off shelves or off the mantlepiece, urinating on the floor or furniture, and putting clothing down the toilet. A second category included less damaging disruption of the same sort, involving deliberate untidying of the house. The third category comprised deliberate heavy-handedness in putting objects down: banging them down on table or work surface (sometimes but not always causing cups or plates to break). The fourth category was made up of a variety of other forms of disturbance: hitting others, pulling at other people's clothing, and pulling her own clothing.

An overcorrection approach was adopted to discourage these behaviours. This involved both restitution of the environment and massed positive practice of specific alternative behaviours. "Overcorrection" is a term applied to a punishment procedure which avoids inflicting physical hurt or giving severe reprimands. It involves making a prolonged period of correct activity the consequence of the inappropriate act, either to remove the consequences of the inappropriate act by making good and improving the environment (restitution) or to do the correct form of the inappropriate act many times (massed positive practice). In either form, the activity is sufficient to make the person prefer to avoid it in the future.

Our analysis of the causes of Linda's changed behaviour was rudimentary; it generated little more than an assumption that Linda was displaying opposition to staff and the structure of household life generally. The overcorrection procedure was designed to demonstrate to her that behaving in such a manner would not be tolerated. Linda was still living a divided life at this time, partly in the house and partly in the family home. Staying in the family home remained a frequent occurrence but the visits had lost all pattern. She sometimes went home at weekends. At other times she went during the week and stayed in the house at weekends. On yet other occasions, she went home for a complete week, including the weekend before and the one after. The person-in-charge of the house and the community psychologist visited Linda's family to discuss the problems being presented and the proposed strategy to deal with them. They also discussed whether it would be in Linda's best interests to make her visits home more regular and not quite so frequent, such as every other weekend. Linda's family were surprised that Linda was causing such problems but gave their support to the management strategy proposed, including regular but less frequent visiting. They were surprised because it had always seemed to them that Linda was happy living at 10 Summerton Road. She had always seemed happy to return there after staying at their house.

The precise management strategies adopted varied according to the nature of the disturbance. They all had the character of causing Linda to practise an alternative, pro-social behaviour and of ensuring that she restored the environment to a state at least as good, if not better, than before. Staff acted in a neutral, controlled, and dispassionate manner. Compared with the somewhat inconsistent negative and emotional reactions which are usual when individuals have difficulty living together, the controlled and premeditated nature of procedures of this kind appears artificial. However, the consistency and absence of emotional associations have a function. The intention is to communicate to the individual that other people do not like the particular behaviour, not that they do not like the individual. Therefore, when the overcorrection has been completed, and at all other times, the person is treated positively and warmly. Staff have to avoid carrying over a negative attitude from the period of disruption to other times. The fact that they have made a controlled response to each specific presenting problem should enable them to leave every incident behind them after dealing with it.

Overcorrection procedures tend to be time-consuming. Those used with Linda were no exception. Specifically, for damaging objects or making a mess, Linda had to sweep up all visible mess, throw away debris, wash or vacuum the area affected, wash or vacuum the rest of the floor, and replace all furniture moved during the process of clearing up. In all, this would occupy a minimum of ten minutes. For untidying, throwing, and banging down objects, Linda had to replace all items moved out of place, and pick up items dropped or banged, first holding them out for fifteen seconds and then putting them down, in their place or on a surface, gently. She would then have to pick them up, hold them, and put them down again gently a total of twenty times. For pulling staff's clothing or her own, or for hitting other people, Linda had to engage in an arm exercise for five minutes. This involved first holding her arms out at her side for fifteen seconds, then holding them above her head for fifteen seconds, and then holding them straight out in front of her for fifteen seconds, repeating the cycle to fill the time.

Practicalities in following the programme had to be considered. Matters such as what to do if the disruption occurred when Linda was having a bath or a meal, how to ensure other members of the household were as unaffected as possible, and how to prevent Linda from avoiding the overcorrection effort by escalating the scale of her disruption had to be determined. At the beginning, there was a rota specifically designating one member of on-duty staff as the overcorrection trainer. This rota initially comprised the community psychologist and members of the research team connected with the house. The programme of management was conducted throughout September, October, and November, 1983. After the first three weeks, when the frequency of disruptions had declined, management was taken over by the staff of the house. Records of disruption and implementation of the procedure were kept throughout. These records showed that the "messy" disruptions fell from an average of six per day in the first nine days of the programme to one per day over the next nine days, still averaging one per day in the first nine days of November. "Noisy" disruptions averaged sixteen per day during the first nine days, five per day during the second nine days, and two per day during the first nine days of November. "Pulling" disruptions averaged thirty-six, twelve, and two per day for similar periods. This last category included Linda pulling other people's clothing or hair as well as pulling her own clothing, in particular pulling up her dress at the back as she walked. This behaviour was resistant to change, probably being part of her already-mentioned set of self-stimulatory behaviours. It was not considered an important target to change at this stage. More importantly, the disruption of household life and attacks on staff had virtually disappeared.

We were not altogether satisfied with this episode, or the content and the operation of the programme. There was a feeling that it had been rushed into without adequate prior analysis because of the seriousness of the presenting problems. It served the function of retrieving the *status quo* and cutting short the development of a repertoire of extremely disruptive acts. As a side effect, it had also caused a beneficial change in Linda's living conditions. Linda now had a regular pattern of living primarily in 10 Summerton Road and going for routine stays with her family. The house staff (who have shown great commitment to attaining what they judged to be in the best interests of the people living at the house) did not take easily to implementing the overcorrection. Moreover, the programming issues which had been of concern before — how to gain Linda's cooperation generally and in a more ordinary way, and what to do, if anything, about her self-stimulatory behaviours — still needed to be dealt with.

A more positive approach

The small house service had withstood a period of increased difficulty. The staff at 10 Summerton Road and the staff in the special needs unit had maintained the basic order of their services and their role in other people's lives while also coping with the extra difficulties Linda presented. They now looked forward to improving their mode of interaction with Linda to make cooperation and purposeful occupation more likely to occur.

During the course of our research, video recordings had been taken of all the people living in the house as they went about their household business. These revealed substantial differences in the way individual members of staff interacted with Linda in the course of the same day. Some staff tried to gain her cooperation almost entirely by asking her to do something. When she responded by ignoring their request, saying "No", or escalating her self-stimulatory noises and movements, they simply repeated their request. There were examples of staff asking something of Linda upwards of ten times in a row to no avail. In the course of this, Linda would refuse by shouting, throwing her head back violently, stamping, banging surfaces with her hand, or displaying other similar forms of disruption. In contrast, other staff asked Linda to do something just once and offered her physical guidance immediately if she did not respond. She usually followed the request with the help given. Whereas the first interactional pattern is likely to teach Linda how to avoid an activity, the second may teach her the desirability of joining in. Even when Linda reached a high pitch of refusal, if staff gave her some physical guidance, there was a good chance of her calming down and joining in.

On the basis of these observations, the community psychologist devised a new programme for Linda, to be implemented first in the special needs unit and then in the house. The primary aim was to increase Linda's participation and promote staff interaction with her when she was usefully engaged in activity. In both settings the programme involved staff observing each other at work with Linda, filling in a specially devised recording form, and sharing with each other their own interpretation of the extent to which the balance of their interactions with Linda showed praise after she had cooperated with their verbal requests. The procedure for staff working with Linda was set out as follows:

1. *Clarify the tasks to be done as a set of discrete steps. Be prepared to give Linda a verbal prompt on each step.*

2. *Before you say anything to Linda check she is quiet and not making "amping" noises, crying, or being otherwise disruptive. Wait if she is not quiet, looking away from her until she becomes quiet. Do this at each step.*

3. *Say to Linda what you are going to do.*

4. *Give Linda the instruction (verbal prompt) for the first step. Allow her about five seconds to comply (follow the request).*
5. *If Linda does not follow the instruction (stays unresponsive, tries to leave, make noises, says "no") give her just enough physical guidance (physical prompt) to do the step you have asked. You may accompany this help with a repeat instruction if you wish but DO NOT REPEAT THE INSTRUCTION WITHOUT GIVING PHYSICAL ASSISTANCE.*
6. *When Linda follows the instruction with physical guidance, praise her warmly and go on to the next step.*
7. *If Linda carries out the step WITHOUT you giving her a prompt or instruction, praise her very warmly.*
8. *AT NO TIME comment on any noises, attempts to leave, or other disruptive behaviour. DO NOT make any disapproving statement. If Linda becomes noisy wait, without looking at her, until she is quiet, then return to giving her an instruction (or physical guidance if you have already given her the instruction). DO NOT allow Linda to avoid completing the task, but BE VERY POSITIVE IN YOUR PRAISE WHEN SHE GIVES HER COOPERATION, EVEN IF YOU ARE GIVING EXTENSIVE PHYSICAL ASSISTANCE.*

The staff observing were trained to record if Linda was quiet, the number of verbal prompts, whether Linda cooperated after the first prompt, the number of physical prompts, whether staff praised Linda for doing the task, and whether staff made any disapproving statements aimed at stopping Linda from doing something. These data were collected in successive columns, each relating to a discrete component of the task to be done. The data were analysed in terms of the proportion of total tasks (columns) for which (a) Linda was quiet, (b) only one verbal prompt was given, (c) Linda complied, (d) guidance was given because Linda did not comply, (e) praise was given, and, (f) disapproval was given. Staff performance was compared against the standards set for successful implementation of the procedure; 90%, 85%, 90%, 100%, 90% and 0% respectively. The observer was also invited to record any general comments on the session.

The introduction of the component of staff observing each other helped all members of staff to see for themselves some features of their habitual interactions with Linda which differed from what they had thought they were doing. They saw that Linda received praise less often than they had thought and that their primary mode of trying to get her to do something was by verbal request. When that had not been successful, they had simply repeated the request. Rather than seeing Linda as defiant (that is, a person to be viewed unsympathetically), a perception was given of Linda as a woman with a severe mental handicap, with many distracting behaviours and doubtful language capability, who was not getting the direct physical assistance she needed to behave appropriately. This had a generally beneficial effect in changing working practices. Linda's cooperation has increased substantially from this time.

On reflection, our dissatisfaction and self-criticism concerning the relative failure of the home service to cater for Linda's needs and produce some form of positive benefit might be summarised as our having taken a long time to get to first base, something over two years. The outburst of "house-wrecking" behaviour followed a particularly unsettled time, when Linda had spent a week in the house, gone home for the weekend and the following week, come back to the house for the next weekend, gone home during the weekdays of the next week and then from Wednesday to Wednesday after that, been back in the house for seven days and home for five, and back in the house for three days and home for seven. The house staff had been following the policy of promoting free and unconstrained contact with relatives and simply responding to parental requests for Linda to stay with them. The response *to do something* about the problems Linda was presenting to household management reflected the needs of staff more than the careful consideration of Linda's welfare. It should perhaps be regarded as symptom control, where the person with the mental handicap is, wrongly, the exclusive focus of change. Coincidentally, more significant changes were made.

A firm pattern was established as to where Linda lived: 10 Summerton Road became her home. As a by-product of the overcorrection programme, some demonstration was made of the role that staff interactions had in promoting cooperative or oppositional responses by Linda. This may have helped in setting the scene for the success of the far more acceptable programme of management that followed.

Positive developments and the role of the house

While wishing to describe in detail the possible errors in judgement and difficulties that the service has experienced, we do not wish to suggest either that there was nothing good to say about this period or that a residential service with other characteristics or objectives would necessarily have served Linda better. We do not know. It is possible to conceive that if Linda had been provided with a residential arrangement made specifically for her, so that her needs were not constrained by the requirement to also meet the needs of others, her programme of care would have been improved. But the provision of more specialist care is, even today, still confused with the provision of specialist "units" which group people together who are said to share similar characteristics. Linda might be regarded as one of a group which is often singled out for special definition: people who are severely socially impaired, non-responsive, and who engage in ritualistic and other inappropriate behaviours. However, grouping together people who are said to share particular characteristics does not in itself constitute the provision of a specialist service, and it does have some undesirable consequences. Grouping a defined minority of people together implies larger catchment areas and the breakdown of local services. It also implies creating a very different social environment which is defined by the prevailing similarities between group members. It is not logical for the service to create such a social environment unless it is the long-term objective of the service to support its continuance. If not, the creation of such an environment simply compounds the extent of change which must be generated. The objectives of care underpinning the 10 Summerton Road service were consistent with the creation of a normal social existence. However, the extent to which it could achieve that objective has been limited by the number of people and the range of individual needs it sought to serve. Further development is called for: of service models which are smaller in scale, more extensively individualised, and thereby *specialist*.

Even during the unsatisfactory period of confusion and difficulty for Linda, certain positive goals were being achieved. By and large the needs of Linda's relatives were being met. Their daughter had a residential place in a local house which they considered to be well-staffed and to have high material standards. They recognised the positive ethos of the service and trusted it to act in Linda's interests. They were involved in making decisions concerning her care programme through the individual planning system. They believed Linda to be happy at the house; and Linda's sister often expressed her relief that 10 Summerton Road was there, particularly during the times when she was in America. The fact that the service was local had enabled them to maintain a considerable involvement in Linda's life, having her home to stay frequently and as much as they wanted. They also saw that the service was seeking to give Linda responsibility and to develop her involvement and contribution, something which they began to copy when Linda was with them.

Even though the frequent changes between living at the house and living with her family may have confused and unsettled Linda, the importance of her continuing relationship with her family should not be understated. The proximity of the service and the openness and ease with which contact can be arranged means that Linda can see her family regularly. She stays with them every other weekend and they visit her on the alternate weekends. She visits their house for tea on the Thursday before each weekend she stays at 10 Summerton Road. Her parents 'phone her and she 'phones her parents. Not only do her parents and sister get Linda more involved in their household routine when she stays with them but they also join in her activity when they visit 10 Summerton Road.

Successful teaching has also occurred. Linda has one of the highest success rates in the formal skill teaching programmes set. The pattern of staff interaction stressed in the formal teaching session is the same as the staff interaction procedure used routinely to gain her attention and cooperation. Since moving into the house permanently she has learned to prepare a bath and bathe independently (with intermittent checks from staff), to brush her teeth, to make sandwiches, and to prepare cheese on toast. A monitoring system on the range and extent of Linda's participation in household activities was introduced shortly after she had settled in the house. At first, she was involved in about 28 household tasks per week. Now she is involved in about 40, reflecting a growing level of participation in the life of the household. It is true that other people living in the house may have double that amount of involvement and some, who do not go out to day-care services, treble that level of participation, but the records reflect the staff feeling that constructive occupation is on the up for Linda as well.

Linda has lost weight, from between twelve and thirteen stones at the outset to just over nine stones. This has helped to make quite a substantial change in her appearance. Perhaps because her clothes pull less, the habit of pulling and flicking up the back of her dress when getting up and walking has decreased. The reduction in weight has also enabled her to wear trousers.

It is still true that Linda has fewer opportunities for community involvement than others in the house. Our concern to address the issue of her self-stimulatory noises and movements was motivated very much by the knowledge that they acted as a barrier to using community amenities. For example, she went to pubs less frequently than others living in the house and, when she did, the tendency was for her to sit in the garden where her behaviours could be better tolerated than in the bar. Mistakes have been made in trying to find suitable activities for her to pursue in the community. For example, an attempt was made to take her to the cinema. Linda and the member of staff deliberately arrived just as the film was to start. A bag of pop-corn was purchased to provide Linda with a source of activity that it was thought might compete with her "amping" noises. However, she was very noisy in taking her seat and continued to shout a great deal during the opening titles. Moreover, on being given the open bag of pop-corn, she threw it the length of the cinema, spraying out the contents as it went. At that point, they left.

At the same time as the problems of management inside the house were occurring, Linda began to be incontinent quite frequently when in the town centre. Her trips to shops were curtailed. However, as improvements were brought about within the house and in the special needs unit, a programme for reestablishing community involvement was followed. At first, Linda went for short walks with staff in the roads around the house. As these were managed successfully they were gradually extended until she could again take walks to the town centre and back. A beneficial by-product of this deliberate programming was that Linda learned to walk without holding someone else's hand, another contribution to making her a less conspicuous person when out and about in the neighbourhood.

At the moment, Linda's problem stereotypic behaviour appears to be reduced and the prospect of widening her experience of life in the community appears better. Her use of language is now more extensive, she is easier to live with and talk to. She knows the other people who live in the house with her and shows them consideration, sharing things, or passing items at the meal table. It is possible to see different relationships forming between Linda and different members of staff. She likes to know who will be on duty when she returns from the special needs unit and this information is passed on by the house staff so that they can tell Linda when she asks. Some of the beneficial developments experienced by other members of the household have been shared by Linda. A gradual process of fostering pro-social behaviour to the exclusion of her inappropriate conduct has achieved some success and has ensured Linda a local place of residence. We still wonder whether, because of the difficulties involved, we avoided dealing directly with her preference for self-stimulation and her consequent tendency to avoid learning situations and opportunities for participation in general. Whether this avoidance has had, and is continuing to have, a deleterious effect on the situation in which Linda finds herself is still a question which nags us.

REFERENCE

Knowles, W., Masidlover, M. *The Derbyshire Language Scheme Teaching Manual*. (Private publication.) Ripley, 1982.

CHAPTER 8

Concluding remarks

Life goes on

We have described something of the life of one house and nine people with severe and profound mental handicaps over a period of three years. In its relevance to the development of community-based services, it was a critical three years; the initial period being one of the first attempts to look after adults with such a degree of disability in ordinary houses, including some who had been considered disturbed for much of their lives. Eighteen months has passed in the preparation of this book and, although people's stories have continued, we have decided to keep our description within its original boundaries. However we think that a brief sequel to some of the accounts is valuable.

We summarised our concerns about how successful the service had been for Linda by saying that it took a long time to get to first base. Events in the last eighteen months have confirmed this to be true. Linda has begun to experience the kinds of development that have been described for other people. She is more settled now that she lives permanently in the house, but retains an active and good relationship with her local family. Even though staff think she may still prefer to live with her parents, she now clearly lives at 10 Summerton Road. She is involved in the life of the house as a contributor. She talks more, has friends among the staff, and cooperates more easily. She has lost weight, is fitter, and her appearance has changed considerably. She and her family attend her individual programme planning meetings and service staff and family members have good working relationships. Of course, we do not wish to give the impression that all is transformed. Linda requires considerable support and still leads a fairly sheltered life. She also still has many challenging behaviours. We will return later to the absence of long-lasting "cures".

One of the ingredients of life in general is its unpredictability; stability can never be guaranteed. Shirley's job was no more secure than paid employment is for any other member of the working public. The small brewery that operated the pub which she cleaned went out of business, as a result of which she lost her job. Like other unemployed people she has to look for a new job. Unlike other unemployed people she is almost entirely dependent on staff help to do so. The fact that Shirley had a job made it easy to convey to others that her life had changed dramatically. When she lost it, we no longer had that easy route to encapsulate the impact of the greater opportunities Shirley has had since moving from hospital. Nonetheless, the change in her home life was dramatic. She has recently found another job.

Catherine's development has continued in the last eighteen months. The joint effort of her parents and the house staff have brought considerable benefit both to Catherine and to themselves. No new directions have been undertaken but the progress that has been made seems more secure. For a long time we lived with a considerable feeling of vulnerability, fearing that the progress could be lost. Catherine will always be profoundly mentally handicapped and she may still threaten to take her clothes off. But there is a feeling that the development she has achieved has given her sufficient pro-social means of influencing those around her that she will continue to live in a situation which has at least the advantages of 10 Summerton Road if not, in time, something better.

Common themes

It became clear in setting down the detail of each person's story that a number of themes were common to all accounts. The implication is that people with mental handicaps share common experiences whether they have lived in institutional care or the family home. These might be summarised as: limited community participation, to an extent that could be characterised as a failure to achieve citizenship (in its most extreme form, segregation can result even in the loss of community presence); low status and the failure to achieve adulthood; limited support and exposure to opportunities to develop in competence; and a lack of protection of rights and personal interests. The last of these may include failure to receive the kinds of treatment most of us take for granted, such as dental care and prescription of spectacles, or the absence of access to a wide range of activities and experiences which are the stuff of life itself. People who are substantially handicapped typically experience a life of low demand, little expectation of contribution, and no responsibility. This is often equivalent to a life of little variety and low external stimulation; a life which most people would generally perceive as empty and of little interest.

Any service which strives to have impact on these areas of deprivation will therefore need to be active on many fronts if it is to deal with the particular issues relevant to each individual. It is fairly certain that there will be no shortage of ways by which a service *can* act to improve an individual's competence, status, social activities, community participation and contribution, access to treatment and education, and the breadth and intensity of day-to-day activity and experience. If services face the challenge of helping people with substantial handicaps to achieve a life style and a lifetime of experiences similar to those enjoyed by people who are not handicapped there is a huge agenda of work to be done and effective methods to be developed and learned. The task is overwhelming and it is therefore common for services to set objectives only from a relative standpoint: to be generally better than what went before and for an individual to do something different or more than previously.

The service we have described cannot, by any stretch of the imagination, be considered ideal; one which gives the people who depend upon it a fully valued role and position in their local community. By relative judgement, however, it has made some strides towards: re-establishing a community presence for some people and allowing it to continue for others; promoting a life of greater personal responsibility and contribution within the house; promoting a wider variety of interesting or potentially interesting participation in activity; promoting competence, although probably more by a wider application of skills already possessed than by teaching genuinely new motor and cognitive responses; and improving the social status of all of the people described by conspicuous effort to gain a smart, adult appearance and by detailed attention to the content of their activity. (For example, the service users may be perceived as economic contributors to the local community because they do the shopping and pay for the goods purchased, albeit with staff help.)

The area of community participation still has a low level of achievement. The service and its staff have done much which is within their direct power to achieve. In its location, its determination to serve people from the locality, and in its mode of operation, the service has attempted to provide the best possible opportunities for continued or re-established contact between people who have come to live at 10 Summerton Road and their families. Staff have supported members of the household in a high frequency of community use: shopping, using leisure amenities, and going to pubs, cafés, and restaurants. The people living in the house during the last year that these stories cover had, on average, 111 family and friendship contacts; the range being from twenty-three for the person with the least frequent contact to 260 for the person with the most. Contact took the form of people visiting the house, or people from the house going out during the day or for overnight stays away. In addition, people from the house went out to shop, go to a pub, restaurant or café, or to use other community facilities, on an average of 228 occasions in the year, the range being from fifty-two to 415. However, friendships outside of family or staff remain limited and people's contact with the general public is almost entirely at a casual acquaintance level; a few fleeting interactions while shopping or the like. Staff have made efforts to encourage friendships but they are hard to achieve, certainly with that essential element of reciprocity of interest, power, and value which characterises true friendship. Achievement is not entirely absent. Mary has developed friendships and Shirley has visitors who are not immediate family; but it is an area of limited success which may be more closely related to the nature of the service than to the staff's efforts within it. It is still a segregated service in which people with mental handicaps live exclusively with other people with similar handicaps. It is still a service which provides for a relatively large group of people, spanning a considerable range of personal characteristics, competencies, and aptitudes. These factors may constitute considerable barriers which limit the opportunity and basis for the flowering of close personal relationships; ones which add to the barriers inherent in the real functional handicap of the people being served.

Complexity and specialisation

While recognising that problems are still evident in the service, it is important to acknowledge the considerable complexity of issues which staff have attempted to address, and which have been met with some degree of success. What is remarkable is that, at any one time, this span of concern is in the hands and heads of only one person-in-charge, one deputy, and seven other day-time staff. Staff need skills of household organisation, observation and interpretation of behaviour, clarity of statement, teaching, task analysis, routine supportive interaction, talking to people who have difficulty in comprehension and articulation, discussing with families, liaising with other professionals, and demanding action from others in the best interests of the people for whom they are caring. It is not an easy job and they receive scant reward for their expertise. Our aspirations for what can be achieved have grown: there is a growing technology for behavioural analysis and development which needs to be widely mastered: our expectations of what staff must achieve have risen accordingly. Our service structures, however, have not changed to any great extent to allow staff working directly with people with mental handicaps to be rewarded either materially or in terms of status attribution for the specialist expertise they supply.

In looking at the wider service structure, it is also true to say that the responsibility for service quality lies more with the staff than with the managers or providers of the service. Take our concerns about Linda and whether the service was acting in her best interests as an example. These concerns were confined mainly to the service staff. They were not initiated by Linda, by Linda's parents, by any person external to the service who had taken an advocacy role on Linda's behalf, or by the managers of the service. It was satisfactory in all these quarters to continue the *status quo* through a strategy based on containment and working round the problems. Another example is that, in order to do their work effectively, staff need to collect certain information on the experience of each person living in the house, routinely, individual by individual. This monitoring covers the implementation and success rate of teaching, the opportunities given to each person to be involved in household life, and the extent of each one's family contact and use of community amenities. These data give staff a basis for reviewing what they are achieving on behalf of each person. Recording, however, takes time and discipline. Keeping the recording going is largely down to staff diligence and pride in their own rigour. Were they to stop it, it would be interesting to see whether people outside the house would find out that part of the service programme had been dropped.

Not only is the quality of the service largely in the hands of these front-line staff, so too is the safeguarding of service quality. This should not be taken as a criticism of the service managers but as a statement of concern for a vulnerable situation. The manager's position can be appreciated. Relatively few people are being expected to plan and provide the new services which are to replace existing institutions. They are also expected to do this broadly within the expenditure framework of the previously impoverished service. They are expected to establish new modes of operation, train staff, determine the allocation of finance, and be accountable for public expenditure. Some recognition is needed of the complexity that is being demanded of them within a modern definition of accomplishment.

The view we have put forward is that there is a considerable degree of specialism needed within the service staff. We have not defined that specialism in terms of the traditional professional boundaries: psychiatry, psychology, physiotherapy, speech therapy, occupational therapy, and nursing. We believe it is important, however, to stress that we *do* see the business of providing such services as an area of specialism because of an all too common confusion that what is required is ordinariness. The notion of "ordinariness" has been appealed to by people trying to encapsulate the direction of development which residential services should take. However, ordinary, as a descriptor of a life style to be made available by dint of service activity, is very different from ordinary as a descriptor of service process. The former suggests a characterisation of activities, responsibilities, and relationships which, although allowing for a considerable variation in precise detail, might encompass the broad mass of citizens in our society. The latter suggests a limit to the intensity of resources, time, expertise, and service structure which might be directed towards helping a person achieve a desirable outcome. Staff working with people with severe and profound handicaps need to be particularly skilled if they are to make available to these individuals the possibility of a reasonably ordinary life style. For example, one of the classes of staff expertise which is of considerable sophistication is the ability to structure an individual's experience carefully so that the person derives benefit, but without the structure assuming an intensive and conspicuous presence.

One last point concerning the nature of staff specialism. Skill deficiency relative to age is the objective fact upon which the inference of mental handicap is based. As it became apparent that even people with extreme deficiencies were capable of continued learning, service objectives changed from those defined as custodial to those defined as habilitative. The model of service process changed from care to education (although this has not been accompanied by a change in dominant professional groupings). However, although philosophies of education may vary, skill acquisition is not generally seen as an end in itself. Rather skill usage and the growth of experience are more fundamental objectives. Habilitation (skill-acquisition) is a relatively minor component of this service and teaching a similarly minor part of the staff specialism (although the skills involved in teaching are related and extremely relevant to those involved in supporting adaptive behaviour generally). In nearing the end of this book, we are aware that readers may have perceived the central contribution of the house to people's lives as being in the area of skill acquisition. We think that it has been part of the contribution, but that the major part has been the supporting of a wide variety and extent of adaptive participation during every day of the three years covered, where passivity, unpurposeful activity, and inappropriate or damaging behaviour could so easily have been the alternative. Even in this account, progress stands as a proxy for day-to-day participation; it is easier to capture and describe.

Keeping going

The quality of a service is concerned with what service-user behaviours it actually promotes and the means by which it does so. An individual's behaviour is flexible; it changes in response to the current situation. The individual reacts to the current situation from an accumulated history. That accumulated history cannot be taken away. It cannot be eliminated in the same way as an invading bacterium can through the taking of an appropriate antibiotic. Cure is the wrong metaphor.

What we have described in these pages is largely the influence exerted by a service on the way a number of individuals with severe and profound mental handicaps have reacted. The influence has been brought about by changing the situation in which these individuals have found themselves. Considerable experience of such a changed situation may in time alter the balance of accumulated history and the predisposition of the individuals to react in certain ways. But three years, even if people had attained a consistency beyond what in reality has occurred, is a relatively short period compared, for example, with the twenty-two years' prior experience of life that Catherine had known, let alone the half-century of different circumstances for Carol.

If cure is the wrong metaphor, perhaps another can be offered: in order to arrive at the right port, the current course has to be maintained for however long it takes to get there, making adjustments for tides, currents, changing wind direction, and storms along the way. Maintenance of service quality has to be arranged by the service; reliance should not be placed on the constancy of the behaviour of the service user. For example, despite being generally more cooperative, Linda still challenges staff by disarranging the house. Carol too has recently increased the frequency of biting her forearm again. It would be wrong to conclude that past efforts have failed. Past efforts, as we have reported, have been successful in establishing a decline in specific behaviours and a growing maturity or level of cooperation. However, they could not be expected to result in change that would be sustained for the rest of people's lives. Staff now need to look again at how they are interacting with Linda and Carol. They may have failed to maintain in their own behaviour a pattern of interaction which was relevant to the previous success; a fact made more likely by staff turnover. It may be that greater precision is required; a precision which is attainable by repeating the analytic process which worked before. Like any other form of activity, practice improves skill and precise definition concentrates analysis. The problem is that this need to retread familiar paths may lower staff morale if their model of human behaviour suggests permanent solutions without the possibility of future regression. At its most extreme form, interpretation that previous intervention failed because it did not result in permanently enduring improvement may prevent staff re-adopting successful strategies. Staff may lose direction if they lose faith in operational procedures and have no better explanations or perspectives to put in their place. Services should be seen as always being vulnerable to deterioration, and the quality of service operation needs therefore to be maintained by appropriately responsive management, in much the same way as staff fulfil their responsibility for the behaviour of the people in their care.